SINGING IN SIGNS

Hymns and Choruses for the Deaf

COMPILED & REVISED BY CATHY RICE

THOMAS NELSON PUBLISHERS
NASHVILLE

Note: Throughout this book we have capitalized all pronouns, names and references to Deity. We realize that the rules of grammar do not cap such pronouns as who, whose or whom, but we have done so in order that the interpreter will know instantly that the pronoun refers to Deity.

Published in Nashville, Tennessee, by Thomas Nelson, Inc., Publishers and distributed in Canada by Lawson Falle, Ltd., Cambridge, Ontario.

Printed in the United States of America.

Library of Congress Cataloging in Publication Data

Rice, Cathy.
  Singing in signs.

  Includes indexes.
  1. Hymns, English. 2. Sign language. I. Title.
BV465.D4R5   264'.2   81-18830
ISBN 0-8407-9006-6   AACR2

To my
"SPECIAL CHILD" BETTY RICE CABBAGE
who has taught me so many wonderful and
valuable lessons about the nonhearing world.
It was from Betty I learned the joy and pleasure
the deaf receive from music. They do indeed
have music in their hearts and on their hands!

CONTENTS

ACKNOWLEDGEMENTS

I especially appreciate the help of Kaye Rice Fitzgerald for her valuable help in making these songs understandable to the deaf and of Carlene Camp for her help in compiling the choruses.

We have made every effort to locate the copyright holders of the lyrics included in this book. Many of the songs are in the public domain and can be found in most hymnals. Below is a list of song titles and their copyright holders, along with the page number where the lyrics appear. We want to thank the publishers and individuals who granted us permission, not only to print the lyrics but also to alter them when necessary.

BELIEVE ON THE LORD JESUS CHRIST (page 146). Copyright 1920. Renewal 1948 extended by Hope Publishing Co., Carol Stream, IL 60187. All rights reserved. Used by permission.

BLESSED REDEEMER (page 88). Harry Dixon Loes. Copyright 1921. Renewal 1949. Copyright extended. Assigned to Singspiration, Division of The Zondervan Corporation. All rights reserved. Used by permission.

BURDENS ARE LIFTED (page 143). Copyright 1952. Renewal 1980 by John M. Moore. Assigned to Singspiration, Division of The Zondervan Corporation. All rights reserved. Used by permission.

CHRIST FOR ME! (page 142). Copyright 1941. Renewal 1969 by Alex Burns. Assigned to Singspiration, Inc. All rights reserved. Used by permission.

COMING AGAIN (page 141). © Copyright 1957 by Singspiration, Inc. All rights reserved. Used by permission.

CONSTANTLY ABIDING (page 60). Mrs. Will L. Murphy. Copyright 1908. Renewed 1935 by Nazarene Publishing House. Used by permission.

DOWN FROM HIS GLORY (page 30). Words and arrangement copyright 1921. Renewal 1949 by William E. Booth-Clibborn. Assigned to Zondervan Herman Corporation. All rights reserved. Used by permission.

EVERYDAY WITH JESUS (page 142). © Copyright 1936 by Percy Crawford. Renewed © 1964 by Ruth Crawford. All rights reserved. Used by permission.

FOLLOW, I WILL FOLLOW (page 141). Copyright © 1935 and 1937 by Ross Jungnickel, Inc. Copyrights Renewed, Assigned to Chappell & Co., Inc. (Intersong Music, Publisher). International Copyright Secured. All rights reserved. Used by permission.

FOR GOD SO LOVED THE WORLD (page 142). Copyright 1938. Renewal 1966 by Singspiration, Inc. All rights reserved. Used by permission.

GONE, GONE, GONE (page 139). Copyright 1936. Renewal 1964 by Helen Griggs. Assigned to Singspiration, Inc. All rights reserved. Used by permission.

PREFACE

Many deaf people, especially those who have been deaf from infancy, cannot easily understand the figurative language found in many hymns. Often symbolic or archaic words have no sign and must be spelled out in sign language. The hymns in this book have been altered so that the meaning is retained and each word can be signed in rhythm with the music. Just as a singer does not spell the words of a song, neither do those who sing in signs.

A hymnbook for the deaf generally is not used during a church worship service. The deaf must use their hands to sing, and so obviously they cannot hold a book at the same time. In a worship service, the deaf sing along with an interpreter. But to learn their favorite hymns and choruses, the deaf will use this book at home. If you are deaf, we hope this hymnbook will help you as you make "melody in your heart to the Lord."

The interpreter for the deaf will find this book an invaluable resource for his or her work. Deaf people have a thought pattern of their own, and a good interpreter is one who is continually learning to "think deaf." When interpreting hymns and choruses, the interpreter must rapidly think of how to change certain words so the deaf audience will understand and, at the same time, maintain a musical rhythm. This is no easy task when standing before a deaf audience in a church service. This book, then, will enable the interpreter to learn the sign language version of familiar hymns and choruses.

A WORD TO INTERPRETERS

Music is an important part of any church ministry to the deaf. The deaf love music! Not only is it important to interpret the hymns of the regular church service, but good music is an essential part of any Sunday school program for the deaf.

Perhaps you are wondering why deaf people love music. They can feel it! The deaf are very sensitive to vibration. Because our hearing often interferes with this special sense of touch, we cannot "feel" the noise and sounds around us.

I have observed Betty (my deaf daughter) sitting in church and holding onto a songbook, touching the bench in front of her, or placing her feet firmly on the floor. This way she can feel the vibrations from the music. She especially loves a good organ with a strong bass! Try this yourself sometime. You will be surprised at how much you can "hear" through your feet and hands.

I have often asked a deaf person, "Can you feel that?" He will quickly touch or pick up an object near-by, because sometimes sound will cause an object to vibrate enough for the deaf person to feel it.

One time a deaf man came to visit us, and when he drove up to our office I could hear the radio blaring in his car. When he came inside, I told him the radio was on in his car.

"Yes, I know it," he answered. I asked him why he would have the radio blaring when he couldn't hear it. He told me that though he could not hear it, he could feel it. He said this kept him company as he drove mile after mile.

When I was five years old, my family moved to Wichita Falls, Texas. My father was starting a new business, and to help make ends meet, my parents rented out two rooms in our house. A lovely deaf couple with a little five-year-old boy rented these rooms. This was my first exposure to deaf people.

We had a player piano, and the deaf man would often come to our living room and ask permission to play it. He couldn't hear it, but he could sure feel it in his feet, in his body, and in his hands as he sat there pumping and pumping away!

In the summertime during our camp season I sometimes play an accordion. The deaf people who happen to be with us during those weeks always want to put their hands on my accordion so they can "feel" the music.

INTERPRETING MUSIC FOR THE DEAF

Interpreting a song is different from interpreting a sermon. When singing in signs, deaf people learn to follow an interpreter. You may need to instruct the uninitiated to follow as you lead, to sing (sign) slowly, rapidly, hold some words, etc. It's up to you to teach the deaf audience rhythm.

As an example of how to do this, let's look at the first phrase of the chorus, "Jesus, Jesus, Jesus, Sweetest Name I Know." Be sure this is done with rhythm. Keep up with the congregation as they sing these words. You should sign, "Jesus, Jesus, Je-sus," holding the last "Jesus" to fit the rhythm of the song. Then sign "Sweet-est name I know," holding the words "sweetest" and "know" in rhythm with the music. Following the beat of the song, continue with "Fills my ev-'ry long-ing. . . ." Sign the song in a flowing, easy manner. Keep up with the tempo of the hearing congregation.

I have watched song leaders for the deaf who interpret songs just as they interpret sermons. They sign rapidly, "Jesus, Jesus, Jesus, sweetest name I know." Then they stand there and wait for the congregation to catch up, or else they go on with the next phrase ahead of the congregation. Some song leaders "talk" through a song and are finished long before the music stops. The deaf sit there, wondering what has happened! They wonder why the interpreter is not signing the rest of the song. That's why signing with the rhythm of the song is so important if the deaf are to enjoy singing in signs. A flowing, beautiful rhythm makes each song unique.

In some instances, to keep the rhythm, you may have to make a sign twice. An example of this is seen in "Wonderful Words of Life." In this song is the phrase, "Sing them over again to me, wonderful words of life." To make this fit the rhythm, it should be sung, "Sing them o-ver a-gain to me, won-der-ful words of life." You should sign the words "wonder-ful" and "words" twice to maintain the rhythm.

Another example where this is necessary is, "Where He Leads Me I Will Follow." When you sign the word "leads" you must hold it according to the timing of the song. The same is true for the word "follow."

You will find that among workers with the deaf some are more qualified than others for signing music. You need a person who can sign in a beautiful, flowing, rhythmic fashion, who can lead the deaf in a soul-stirring song service.

Of course, this takes practice. No one is born with this ability. The more musically inclined, by practice, practice, and more practice, should be able to attain a beautiful, flowing singing in signs. There is nothing in this world prettier to me than watching a person interpret a song service in a flowing, graceful manner.

While you are teaching deaf people the difference between singing and speaking, teach them to sing with their voices! This, of course, should be done in classes or group meetings for the deaf alone—not in the congregational song service.

Once inhibitions are overcome, the deaf love to sing with their voices. Many deaf people are conscious of their voices and realize they sound different from hearing people. But you can help them shed their self-consciousness when they are grouped together. Soon they will turn loose and sing with real fervor!

SONG SELECTION

You must discover which songs deaf people enjoy "singing." The songs you choose should fit the occasion. Sometimes you will need songs with enthusiasm, some for fun; but certainly you need to choose songs that get into the very soul of the deaf, songs that will bless their lives.

I can still remember songs I sang as a child. Many songs I learned in booster choirs and junior choirs had a tremendous influence on my life. Today, when I hear those songs, they still thrill me. You need to choose songs that can become part of a deaf person's life—songs they will like to sing when they are alone.

We sing a number of choruses and hymns at the Bill Rice Ranch each summer during our camps for the deaf. One of these is "Mine, Mine, Mine, Mine, Jesus is mine." The deaf can easily sign "Mine, Mine, Mine, Mine," and they can sing it with their voices as well.

Another favorite is "I Have the Joy, Joy, Joy, Joy, Down in My Heart." Another is "Hallelu, Hallelu, Hallelu, Hallelujah, Praise Ye the Lord." Often this is done with actions and signs. When the girls sing "Hallelu, Hallelu, Hallelu, Hallelujah," they stand. Then they sit down and the boys stand and sing, "Praise ye the Lord."

We have found that deaf Christians love "When We All Get to Heaven" and "More, More About Jesus." You ought to hear and see the deaf youngsters at camp each summer when they sing the "shout" in the song "When We All Get to Heaven"! Anyone who thinks deaf people can't make noise ought to hear these young people when they sing this song. They sing and "shout the victory" so loudly they almost raise the roof off our auditorium!

SOLOISTS

Did you know there are deaf soloists? This is true. Some deaf people have a natural rhythm in their hands and can sign a song with grace and beauty. My deaf daughter, Betty, is a soloist among the deaf. To see her sing in signs is beautiful and touching.

So, just as some hearing people have beautiful voices, the Lord has given the gift of singing in signs to various deaf individuals. In your work with the deaf you ought to seek out those who seem to have this ability and train them to do solo work in your Sunday school department, in your little get-togethers, and for the entire church congregation.

PRONOUNS

We need to learn to avoid pronouns as we lead the deaf in singing or as we interpret a song service. Rhyme does not mean much to a deaf person. Therefore, you need not worry about losing the rhyme if you change the words as you interpret the song. It is more important that the song be understood than to have the words rhyme.

In the song "He Lives," for example, you want to be sure the deaf audience understands who it is that lives. It would be better to sign this song, "Jesus lives, Jesus lives, Christ Jesus lives today." Now you have established that it is Jesus who lives; therefore you can go on and sign, "He walks with me and talks with me. . . ."

Often in a song, "I" or "Me" refers to "Jesus." But if you sign "I" or "me" the deaf may think you are talking about yourself. So, in cases like these, be sure you use "Jesus," "Lord," or "God"—whichever the "I" or "Me" refers to. An example of this is "Come Unto Me." This should be signed (using the words in brackets to replace words without signs and pronouns):

> Hear the blessed Savior calling the oppressed [burdened].
> O ye heavy laden [troubled], come to Me [Jesus] and rest;
> Come, no longer tarry, I [Jesus] your load will bear,
> Bring Me [Jesus] every burden, bring Me [Jesus] every care.

Chorus:

> Come unto Me [Jesus]; I [Jesus] will give you rest;
> Take My [Jesus] yoke [way] upon you,
> Hear Me [Jesus] and be blessed;
> I [Jesus] am meek and lowly,
> Come and trust My [Jesus] might;
> Come, My [Jesus] yoke [way] is easy,
> And My [Jesus] burden's light.

In the song "Where He Leads Me" you should sign, "Where Jesus leads me I will follow." Do all you can to help the deaf understand whom you are talking about.

In the song "Just As I Am" we have the phrase, "O Lamb of God, I come." If you sign this song to say, "Lamb of God," deaf individuals who are not familiar with Christian symbolism may think you are talking about a lamb. Deaf people often take words literally. So it would be best to change this to say, "O Son of God, I come." Use pronouns or symbolic language very sparingly when interpreting songs.

INTERROGATIVES

Real care and thought should be given to songs that ask questions. The chorus "Isn't He Wonderful?" should be signed thus:

Je-sus is won-der-ful, won-der-ful, won-der-ful,
Je-sus my Lord is won-der-ful.
Eyes have seen, ears have heard,
It is writ-ten in God's Word,
Je-sus my Lord is won-der-ful!

If you sign the question, "Is not Jesus wonderful?" the deaf see the negative and interpret it to say, "Jesus is not wonderful." The only explanation for this is "deaf thinking."

When Betty had her first child, she sent a picture of the baby to my daughter, Kaye, who lived in California at the time. In Kaye's next letter she said, "Isn't Jimmy cute?"

Betty read the letter and said, "Why did Kaye say Jimmy is not cute?"

I looked at Betty and said, "Kaye said Jimmy is cute."

Betty then showed me the letter. "See here," she pointed out, "Kaye says 'isn't' cute."

I explained to Betty that Kaye was saying, "Jimmy is cute, you agree?"

A similar incident happened just recently. A letter came from a preacher inquiring about our adopted deaf son, Ronnie, who was to arrive at the pastor's church at a certain time. The letter said, "I understand Ronnie can't be here until 7:30 P.M."

Ronnie became upset and showed the letter to Betty. "What's wrong?" I asked.

Betty and Ronnie then informed me that this church did not want Ronnie to come for the meeting.

When I read the letter, I knew immediately what the problem was. I knew that the word "can't" had disturbed them. From the "can't," they understood that the preacher did not want Ronnie to come. I again found myself trying to explain the negative. With this in mind, I have found it best to avoid rhetorical questions and negatives in songs.

Dr. Billy Renstrom, a blind soloist who works with us, often sings a song, "Greater Than These." (A real blessing to any heart is to see Billy and Betty sing together. While his clear tenor voice thrills your heart with song, Betty reads his lips and signs the song with her hands.)

This song asks questions and then answers them:

> Is He greater than mountains, all shrouded with trees?
> He's great than these, He's greater than these.
> Is He greater than oceans and turbulent seas?
> He's greater than even these.

Chorus:

> Greater than these, yes, greater than these,
> My Jesus is greater than these;
> So trust Him today, as you fall on your knees,
> For God's Son is far greater than these.

When I interpret this song I make the questions into statements. Here is how I suggest such a song be interpreted:

> Jesus is greater than mountains, all covered with trees.
> He's greater than these [mountains], yes, greater than these.

The word "these" should be changed to "mountains." Since the mountains and seas are not there for you to point to, the object referred to by "these" should be signed.

In the chorus this song has the word "these" several times. The first time I change it to "mountains" and the second time to "these." For the other times, I go back to "mountains."

OTHER HELPS

There are many communication stumbling blocks you need to be mindful of as you interpret a song. For example, in the song, "Coming Again," remember to sign this song to show Jesus coming from heaven. As you sign, "Com-ing a-gain, com-ing a-gain," make your sign of Jesus coming from heaven to you. Do not make the sign of Jesus coming toward you laterally.

Often in songs we sing, "into my heart." Be sure when you sign this to put the "into" into your heart. Do not make the sign "into" going into your hand in front of you. Put your left hand over your heart and put it "into" your heart!

We frequently sing songs which tell us about something that will happen "some day." Naturally, we know this refers to a day in the future; therefore it should be signed "future day." The sign we know for "some" means a piece of something: "some bread," "some candy," "some fruit."

A good example of this is "Some Bright Morning." This should be signed:

> Be not weary, for labor [work] will cease [stop]
> Some [future] glad morning.
> Turmoil [trouble] will change into infinite [forever] peace.
> Some [future] bright morning.

Chorus:

> Some [future] bright morning. Some [future] glad morning.
> When the sun is shining in the eternal sky;
> Some [future] bright morning. Some [future] glad morning,
> We shall see the Lord of Harvest [Savior]
> By and by [future, future, future].

SPELLING

Try never to spell when signing a song. When you spell you are certain to lose rhythm. If and when you come to a word with no sign, try to substitute a word for the one with no sign. For example, in "All Hail the Power of Jesus' Name" there is no sign for the word "hail." If you spell "h-a-i-l" you will lose rhythm. A good substitute in this case would be, "All praise the power of Jesus' name."

Then notice the next phrase, "Let angels prostrate fall." This could be changed to, "Let angels kneel and bow." The next phrase reads, "Bring forth the royal diadem." This can be changed to, "Bring forth the beautiful crown." The next phrase is, "Ye chosen seed of Israel's race." This can be changed to, "Ye chosen people who belong to God." This does not rhyme, but it does mean the same thing, and it helps the deaf to understand the song.

SOME EXPLAINING

Certain songs need to be explained. Before the service starts, if you realize there is going to be a song which is almost impossible to interpret, prepare the deaf audience ahead of time. For example, the song "There Is a Fountain" begins, "There is a fountain filled with blood, drawn from Immanuel's veins." While the introduction is being played you have time to do a little explaining. Give the audience the name of the song and tell them that this is a song full of pictures about Jesus, a song about the blood of Jesus. You can say, "Jesus died on the cross for you. He gave His blood for you." The song can then be interpreted this way:

> There is a cross filled with blood
> Coming from Jesus' body;
> And sinners under that blood,
> Lose all their fill of sin.

Another song that needs an explanation is "Bring Them In." During the introduction, explain that this song is about sheep and the Shepherd. Explain that the Shepherd is a picture of Jesus, and the sheep is a picture of people being saved.

"Leaning on the Everlasting Arms" is another song that might be misunderstood. Explain that the song is about depending on Jesus.

Be conscious of the fact that some deaf people have a limited vocabulary. Whenever you are signing a song or speaking to the deaf, be aware of vocabulary that may need an explanation.

Some time ago I was in a church in Ohio, interpreting a solo at one of the services. The song had the word "grace" in it. As I signed the word "grace" I noticed a sort of blank look on the faces of some of the deaf people. I stopped interpreting and asked, "Do you understand the word 'grace'?"

A deaf man in the audience had been pointed out to me as a very smart man who knew much about the Bible. In fact, he was the teacher for the deaf Sunday school class. When I asked what the word "grace" meant, I was surprised when this man answered, "That's a girl's name."

It would have been foolish for me to go on with the song since few understood what was being sung. I certainly did not want them to think the song was about a girl. I took time to explain the word and then caught up with the finish of the song.

BE PREPARED

As an interpreter for the deaf, you should consider music an important aspect of your church's ministry to the deaf. Don't wait until you get to Sunday school to thumb through a book to find songs to sing. And don't wait until you stand up before the deaf audience in the church auditorium to wonder what is going to be sung and if you will be able to interpret correctly. Preparation should be made beforehand. If you are in charge of music for the church's deaf ministry, your job ought to be important enough to you to do work ahead of time and to be prepared.

Go through your church's hymnal and practice interpreting the songs most frequently used. Change any lyrics you believe would be misunderstood and make notes of these changes. This hymnbook is designed to aid you in this task.

For further preparation, stand before a mirror and practice singing. Go over the hymns again and again. Get them into your heart, into your soul, and into your hands! When you interpret a song, it should come with ease and freedom. This does not happen by accident—it comes from long hours of practice.

You need to know ahead of time what hymns are going to be sung in each service. Ask the choir director to keep you informed in advance. Then, look over the hymns ahead of time, change any words that need to be changed, and practice until you can sign with ease.

By all means, find out what special solos and choir numbers will be used. Often these selections are unfamiliar or wordy. You need time to plan and prepare so you can give the very best to the deaf in the audience.

When there is an instrumental solo, I think it is helpful if the interpreter knows and signs the lyrics of the music being played, if there are any. In a church revival meeting, I learned that a young man would be playing a trumpet solo. I found out what he would be playing, and so as he played, I interpreted the accompanying lyrics. When I finished, a little old deaf lady (she was past seventy) asked me, "Does a horn play words?"

I told her it did not and asked what would make her think it did. When she said, "You interpreted the words," I was surprised. I explained to her that I had asked ahead of time what the man would be playing. I told her I had wanted her to be a part of every bit of the service, and so I had interpreted the song so she could know what he was playing. She was so appreciative of this.

Don't forget, music should be and can be a vital part of your church's deaf ministry. Once my husband was preaching in a northern church. After the service, a deaf teen-ager came forward to speak to me. In his hand he had an old, battered songbook. It was one of the first ones we printed at the Bill Rice Ranch to help deaf workers interpret song services.

This boy showed the songbook to me and said, "My book—I love it!" He then opened the book to a certain page and said, "This is my favorite song. I love this song because Jesus saved me."

I was anxious to see what the song was. It was "Oh, How I Love Jesus." I noticed he had changed a few words. As you know, the song says, "There is a name I love to hear." Above the word "hear" he had written "sing." The next phrase says, "It sounds like music to my ear." He had changed it to, "It sounds like music to me."

He pointed to the song and asked, "True? Jesus first loved me?"

I answered, "Yes, Jesus did first love you."

With a smile on his face he said, "I love this song because Jesus first loved me!"

From the worn look of the book I could tell that he had spent many hours leafing through it.

Ephesians 5:19 says, "Speaking to yourselves in psalms and hymns and spiritual songs, singing and making melody in your heart to the Lord" (KJV).

Deaf people can certainly make melody in their hearts to the Lord. Remember, you can help the deaf know the blessing of music.

I. HYMNS FOR WORSHIP

DOXOLOGY* 1

Praise God, from Whom all blessings come,
Praise Him, all people here on earth;
Praise Him above, you angels in heaven;
Praise Father, Son, and Holy Spirit. Amen.

ALL HAIL THE POWER 2

1. All praise the power of Jesus' name!
   Let angels kneel and bow,
   Bring here the royal crown,
   And crown Jesus, Lord of people.
   Bring here the royal crown,
   And crown Jesus, Lord of people.

2. You chosen people who belong to God,
   You saved from all sin,
   Praise God Who saves you by His grace,
   And crown Jesus, Lord of people.
   Praise God Who saves you by His grace,
   And crown Jesus, Lord of people.

3. Let every person, every one,
   On this world around,
   To God all kingly honor give,
   And crown Jesus, Lord of people.
   To God all kingly honor give,
   And crown Jesus, Lord of people.

4. O that with all saved people,
   We at Jesus' feet can bow;
   We will join the everlasting song,
   And crown Him, Lord of people.
   We will join the everlasting song,
   And crown Him, Lord of people.

---

*See the ACKNOWLEDGMENTS for a listing of hymns, choruses, and their copyright holders. Any titles not listed are believed to be in the public domain.

3 DOWN FROM HIS GLORY

1. Down from His glory, always living story,
   My God and Savior came, and Jesus was His name.
   Born in a poor place, not accepted by man,
   Jesus, man of sorrow, tears, and suffering.

Chorus:
   O how I love God; how I adore Him!
   My breath, my sunshine, my all in all is He!
   The great Maker became my Savior,
   And all God's goodness lives in me.

2. Wonderful! Jesus came to bring us redemption.
   When we were in sin without hope in the world,
   Jesus' kind soft heart gave up His glory in heaven,
   To come to earth to love and save my soul.

4 WOUNDED FOR ME

1. Wounded for me, wounded for me
   There on the cross He was wounded for me;
   Gone my sins, and now I am free,
   All because Jesus was wounded for me.

2. Dying for me, dying for me,
   There on the cross He was dying for me;
   Now in His death my salvation I see,
   All because Jesus was dying for me.

3. Living for me, living for me,
   Up in the heaven He is living for me;
   Daily He's begging and praying for me,
   All because Jesus is living for me.

4. Coming for me, coming for me,
   One day to earth He is coming for me;
   Then with what joy His dear face I shall see,
   Oh, how I praise Him! He's coming for me.

SOLDIERS OF THE CROSS 5

If you love God, why not serve Him?
If you love God, why not serve Him?
If you love God, why not serve Him?
Soldiers of the cross.

Sinner, will you take my Jesus?
Sinner, will you take my Jesus?
Sinner, will you take my Jesus?
And be soldiers of the cross.

SWEET HOUR OF PRAYER 6

1. Sweet hour of prayer! Sweet hour of prayer!
   That calls me from a world of worry,
   And calls me to my Father's throne
   Make all my wants and wishes known;
   In times of trouble and of sadness.
   My soul has many times found rest,
   And many times left tempter's sin
   By your answer, sweet hour of prayer.

2. Sweet hour of prayer! Sweet hour of prayer!
   By prayer will my asking go
   To Him whose truth and faithfulness
   Join the waiting soul to bless;
   And because He begs me pray to Him,
   Believe His Word and trust His grace,
   I'll give to Him my every worry,
   And wait for you, sweet hour of prayer.

3. Sweet hour of prayer! Sweet hour of prayer!
   Can I your comforting share,
   Till, from the end of my life,
   I see my home, and go to heaven:
   This body of flesh I'll leave, and rise
   To get the everlasting gift;
   And shout, while going through the air,
   Goodbye, goodbye, sweet hour of prayer.

7 LORD, I'M COMING HOME

1. I've wandered far away from God,
   Now I'm coming home;
   The paths of sin long time I've walked,
   Lord, I'm coming home.

Chorus:
   Coming home, coming home,
   Never more to roam,
   Open wide Your arms of love,
   Lord, I'm coming home.

2. I've wasted many a precious year,
   Now I'm coming home;
   I now say "forgive" with bitter tears,
   Lord, I'm coming home.

3. I am tired of sin and straying, Lord,
   Now I'm coming home;
   I'll trust Your Word, believe Your Word,
   Lord, I'm coming home.

4. My soul is sick, my heart is heavy,
   Now I'm coming home;
   My strength is new, my hope again,
   Lord, I'm coming home.

8 THIS WORLD IS NOT MY HOME

1. This world is not my home; I am only passing through.
   My riches are put in somewhere beyond the sky.
   The angels call to me from heaven's open door,
   And I can't feel at home in this world no more.

2. O Lord, You know I have no friend like You,
   If heaven is not my home then, Lord, what will I do?
   The angels call to me from heaven's open door,
   And I can't feel at home in this world no more.

1. When we walk with the Lord
   In the Light of His Word
   What a glory Jesus shines on our way!
   While we do His good wants,
   He will live with us always,
   With all people who will trust and obey.

Chorus:
   Trust and obey, for there's no other way
   To be happy in Jesus,
   But to trust and obey.

2. Not a shadow can rise,
   Not a cloud in the skies,
   But Jesus' smile quickly makes go away;
   Not a doubt nor a fear,
   Not a trouble nor a tear,
   Can abide while we trust and obey.

3. Not a burden we have,
   Not a sorrow we have,
   But our work Jesus will much pay;
   Not a grief nor a loss,
   Not a frown nor a cross,
   All is blessed if we trust and obey.

4. But we never can prove
   The joys of Jesus' love
   Until all we have given to Him;
   For the love that He shows,
   And the joy He gives us,
   Are for all who will trust and obey.

5. Then in fellowship sweet
   We will sit at Jesus' feet,
   Or we'll walk by His side in the way;
   What Jesus says we will do,
   Where He sends we will go,
   Never fear, only trust and obey.

1. Stand up, stand up for Jesus,
   You soldiers of the cross!
   Lift high Jesus' royal flag,
   It must not be lost;
   From victory to victory,
   Jesus' army will He lead,
   Until every enemy is destroyed,
   And Christ is Lord truly.

2. Stand up, stand up for Jesus,
   The trumpet call obey,
   Forth to the mighty conflict,
   In this His glorious day;
   "Ye that are men now serve Him"
   Against unnumbered [not counted] foes,
   Let courage rise with danger,
   And strength to strength oppose.

3. Stand up, stand up for Jesus
   Stand in His strength alone;
   The bodily strength will fail you,
   You must not trust yourself:
   Know the good news about Jesus,
   And always be in prayer,
   Maybe duty calls, maybe danger,
   Be ready to go there.

4. Stand up, stand up for Jesus,
   This life will not be long;
   Today we fight with Devil,
   Tomorrow in heaven we'll sing:
   To you that go to heaven,
   Eternal life you'll have;
   And with the King of Glory
   You will live eternally!

1. I have found a friend in Jesus,
   He's everything to me,
   He's the best of ten thousand to my soul;
   Jesus, the flower of the valley,
   In Jesus alone I see
   All I need to cleanse and make me free from sin.
   In sorrow Jesus my comfort,
   In trouble Jesus my help,
   Jesus tells me every worry to give Him:
   Jesus, the flower of the valley,
   The bright and morning star,
   Jesus, the best of ten thousand to my soul.

2. Jesus all my griefs has taken,
   And all my sorrows borne;
   In temptation He's my strong and powerful help;
   I have all for Jesus left,
   And all my wants destroyed from my heart,
   And now He keeps me by His power.
   If all the people leave me,
   And Satan tempt me much,
   With Jesus I will truly go to heaven:
   Jesus, the flower of the valley,
   And the bright and morning star,
   He's the best of ten thousand to my soul.

3. He will never, never leave me,
   And not forget me here,
   While I live by faith and do His blessed wants;
   Angels are all around me,
   I've nothing now to fear,
   With His love Jesus my empty soul will fill.
   Then going up to heaven to see His blessed face,
   Where times of joy will ever be:
   Jesus, the flower of the valley,
   The bright and morning star.
   He's the best of ten thousand to my soul.

12 CHRIST RECEIVETH SINFUL MEN

1. Sinners Jesus will receive;
   Tell this word of grace to all
   Who the heavenly pathway leave,
   All who wait here, all who fall.

Chorus:
   Sing it more and more again;
   Christ receives sinful men;
   Make the preaching clear and easy;
   Christ receives sinful men.

2. Come, and He will give you rest;
   Trust Him, for His word is clear;
   He will take the sinful person;
   Christ receives sinful men.

3. Now my heart is sinful not,
   Pure before the law I stand;
   He who cleansed me from all sin,
   Satisfied the last demand.

4. Christ receives sinful men,
   Yes, me too with all my sin;
   Cleaned from every dirty sin,
   Heaven with Him I enter in.

13 THE CREATION

1. And God said the sun should shine,
   The rain should fall, the flowers should grow,
   And God said the birds should sing,
   And it was true, was true.

2. And God said the grass should grow,
   The trees bear fruit, the winds should blow,
   And God said the streams should flow,
   And it was true, was true.

1. Hear the heavenly angels sing,
   Glory to the newborn King;
   Peace on earth, and mercy sweet,
   God and sinners joined.
   Joyful all you people rise,
   Join the victory in the skies,
   With the angel hosts tell,
   Christ is born in Bethlehem.

Chorus:
   Hear! The heavenly angels sing,
   Glory to the newborn King.

2. Christ, by angels in heaven worshipped,
   Christ the everlasting Lord;
   Arrive in time, behold Jesus come,
   Born of a virgin,
   Born in flesh, God the Father see,
   Praise God, Who now comes in a body!
   Pleased as a man to come to people,
   Jesus our Savior here.

3. Praise the heaven-born Prince of Peace!
   Praise the Son of Righteousness!
   Light and life to all Jesus brings,
   Risen with saving in His life.
   In love He leaves His glory in heaven,
   Born that man no more may die;
   Born to raise the sons of earth;
   Born to give people second birth.

4. Come, Jesus, desire of all nations,
   Make in us Thy humble home,
   Rise, the woman's conquering Son,
   Kill in us the Devil's way;
   All sin now take from my heart,
   Put Jesus' love now in its place:
   Now Jesus from heaven above,
   Give to us Thy perfect love.

15 O LITTLE TOWN OF BETHLEHEM

1. O little town of Bethlehem,
   How quiet we see you stay!
   Above the deep and dream not sleep
   The silent stars pass by;
   But in your dark streets shines
   The everlasting Light.
   The hopes and fears of all the years
   Finish in you now.

2. For Christ is born of Mary;
   And gathered all above,
   While people sleep, the angels keep
   Angels' watch of wondering love.
   O morning stars together,
   Tell the holy birth,
   And praises sing to God the King,
   And peace to men on earth.

3. How silently, how silently,
   The wondrous Gift is giv'n!
   So God gives to people's hearts
   The blessings of his heav'n.
   No ear may hear His coming;
   But in this world of sin,
   Where weak souls will receive Jesus,
   The dear Christ enters in.

4. O holy Babe of Bethlehem,
   Descend to us, we pray,
   Away our sin and enter in,
   Be born in us now.
   We hear the Christmas angels
   The great glad story tell,
   O come to us, stay with us,
   Our Lord Christ and King.

1. It came upon the midnight clear,
   That glorious song of old,
   From angels coming near the earth
   To touch their harps of gold;
   "Peace on the earth, good will to men,
   From heaven's all gracious King;"
   The world in solemn stillness stay
   To hear the angels sing.

2. Still through the dark skies angels come,
   With peaceful wings unfurled,
   And still their heavenly music floats
   O'er all the weary world;
   Above its sad and lowly plains
   Angels come on hovering wing,
   And much sounds
   The blessed angels sing.

3. And you, beneath life's heavy load,
   Whose bodies are bending low,
   Who toil along the climbing way
   With painful steps and slow,
   Look now! for glad and golden hours
   Come swiftly on to you;
   O rest beside the weary road,
   And hear the angels sing.

4. For now the days are hastening on,
   Seen by preachers past,
   When with the ever circling years
   Comes round the years of gold;
   When peace shall over all the earth
   Its ancient splendors fling,
   And the whole world give back the song
   Which now the angels sing.

17 SILENT NIGHT

1. Silent night, holy night, All is calm, all is bright
   Round yon virgin mother and Child,
   Holy Infant so tender and mild,
   Sleep in heavenly peace, Sleep in heavenly peace.

2. Silent night, holy night, Darkness flies, all is light;
   Shepherds hear the angels sing,
   Alleluia! hail the King!
   Christ the Savior is born, Christ the Savior is born.

3. Silent night, holy night, Guiding Star, lend thy light;
   See the Eastern wise men bring
   Gifts and homage to our King!
   Christ the Savior is born, Christ the Savior is born.

18 O COME, ALL YE FAITHFUL

1. O come all you faithful, joyful and winner,
   O come you, O come you to Bethlehem;
   Come and behold Jesus, born the King of angels;

Chorus:
   O come let us adore Jesus, O come let us adore Jesus,
   O come let us adore Jesus, Christ, the Lord.

2. Sing, choirs of angels, sing in excitement,
   O sing, all you bright angels of heaven above.
   Glory to God, all glory in the highest:

3. Yes, Lord, we welcome you, born this happy morning,
   Jesus, to Thee be all glory given;
   Word of the Father, now in flesh appearing;

1. I love to tell the story
   Of not seen things above,
   Of Jesus and His glory,
   Of Jesus and His love,
   I love to tell the story,
   Because I know true,
   It satisfies my wantings
   As nothing else can do.

Chorus:
   I love to tell the story,
   'Twill be my story in glory
   To tell the old, old story
   Of Jesus and His love.

2. I love to tell the story,
   More wonderful it is
   Than all the wonderful things
   In all our wonderful dreams.
   I love to tell the story,
   It did so much for me;
   And that is the reason
   I tell it now to you.

3. I love to tell the story,
   'Tis pleasant to say again
   What is, each time I tell it,
   More wonderfully sweet.
   I love to tell the story,
   For some have never heard
   The story of salvation
   From God's own holy Word.

4. I love to tell the story,
   For all who know it best
   Are wanting and begging to hear it
   Same as other.
   And when, in heavenly glory,
   I sing the new, new song,
   'Twill be the old, old story
   That I have loved so long.

20 SUNRISE

1. When I will come to the last of my life,
   When I will rest at the end of life's day,
   When "Welcome home" I will hear Jesus say,
   O, that will be sunrise for me.

Chorus:
   Sunrise tomorrow, sunrise tomorrow,
   Sunrise in glory is waiting for me,
   Sunrise tomorrow, sunrise tomorrow,
   Sunrise with Jesus for eternity.

2. When in Jesus' beauty I see the great King,
   Join with Christians Jesus' praises to sing,
   When I join loved ones my song to bring,
   O, that will be sunrise for me.

3. When life is finished and day becomes dark,
   In heaven home my soul is in,
   When I see Jesus my Savior at last,
   Oh, that will be sunrise for me.

21 JUST A CLOSER WALK WITH THEE

1. I am weak but God is strong,
   Jesus keep me from all wrong;
   I'll be satisfied as long,
   As I walk, let me walk close to You.

Chorus:
   Only a closer walk with You,
   Let me Jesus if You please,
   Daily walking close to You,
   Let it be, dear Lord,
   Let it be.

2. Through this world of work and sin,
   If I fall, Lord, who cares?
   Who with me my burden helps?
   None but You, dear Lord, none but You.

IN MY HEART THERE RINGS A MELODY   22

1. I have a song that Jesus gave me,
   It was sent from heaven above,
   There never was a sweeter song
   Than the song of Jesus' love.

Chorus:
   In my heart I have a beautiful song,
   I have a beautiful song, I have a beautiful song:
   In my heart I have a beautiful song,
   I have a beautiful song of Jesus' love.

2. I love the Christ Who died on Calvary
   Because He washed my sins away;
   He put within my heart a song,
   And I know the song will stay.

3. Jesus' love will be my no-end song in heaven,
   With all the saved people I will sing;
   It will be a beautiful song
   When saved people sing in heaven.

I NEED THEE EVERY HOUR   23

1. I need God every hour, most wonderful Lord;
   No other voice like Yours can peace give me.

Chorus:
   I need You, O, I need You; every hour I need You!
   O bless me now, my Savior, I come to You!

2. I need You every hour, stay You near me;
   Temptations lose their power when You are here.

3. I need You every hour, in joy or pain;
   Come fast and live with me, or life is no good.

4. I need You every hour, Most Holy One:
   O make me Yours truly, You blessed Son.

24 ONLY A SINNER

1. Nothing do I have that God not give;
   God gave it because I believed;
   I will not boast, I have no pride;
   I'm only a sinner saved by grace.

Chorus:
   Only a sinner saved by grace!
   Only a sinner saved by grace!
   This is my story—to God is the glory,
   I'm only a sinner saved by grace!

2. One time I foolish and sin bossed my heart,
   Making my walk from God to leave;
   Jesus found me and I am happy now;
   I know I'm a sinner saved by grace.

25 FOLLOW ON

1. Down in the valley with my Savior I would go.
   Where flowers are blooming and sweet waters flow;
   Every place Jesus leads me I would follow, follow on,
   Walking in Jesus' footsteps till the crown be won.

Chorus:
   Follow! Follow! I would follow Jesus!
   Any place, every place, I would follow Him.
   Follow! Follow! I would follow Jesus!
   Every place Jesus leads me I would follow Him.

2. Down in the valley with my Savior I would go,
   Where the storms are sweeping and the dark
       waters flow:
   With His hand to lead me I will never, never fear,
   Danger cannot frighten me if my Lord is near.

3. Down in the valley or upon the mountain high,
   Close beside my Savior would my soul all time keep;
   He will lead me safely in the path that He has trod,
   Up to where they gather on the hills of God.

SAVED TO TELL OTHERS

We're saved, saved to tell other people
Of God's Son who lived on earth;
Saved, saved to live daily
For the Christ of Calvary;
Saved, saved to invite you to His salvation free.
We're saved, saved, saved by Jesus' blood
For all eternity.

PRAISE HIM! PRAISE HIM!

1. Praise Him! Praise Him!
Jesus, our blessed Redeemer!
Sing, O people, Jesus' wonderful love tell all [people].
Praise Him! Praise Him! All you angels in glory;
Strength and honor give to His holy name!
Same as shepherd, Jesus will guard His people,
In His arms Jesus carries them all day long.

Chorus:
Praise Him! Praise Him!
Tell of Jesus' wonderful greatness:
Praise Him! Praise Him!
Always in joyful song!

2. Praise Him! Praise Him!
Jesus, our blessed Redeemer!
For our sins He suffered, and bled, and died;
He, our Rock, our hope of eternal salvation,
Praise Him! Praise Him! Jesus the crucified.
Tell His praises! Jesus Who bore our sorrows,
Love so great, so wonderful, deep and strong.

3. Praise Him! Praise Him!
Jesus, our blessed Redeemer!
Heavenly angels loud with praises sing!
Jesus, Savior, rules forever and ever;
Crown Jesus! Crown Jesus! Preacher and our great
   King.
Christ is coming! Over the world victorious,
Power and glory unto the Lord belong.

28 ONLY TRUST HIM

1. Come, every one by sin saddened,
   There's mercy with the Lord
   And He will truly give you rest
   By trusting in His Word.

Chorus:
   Only trust Him, only trust Him,
      only trust Him now;
   He will save you, He will save you,
      He will save you now.

2. For Jesus gave His wondrous blood,
   Many blessings to give you;
   Be saved now by Jesus' blood
   That washes sins away.

3. Yes, Jesus is the Truth, the Way,
   That leads you into rest;
   Believe in Him without waiting,
   And you are fully blessed.

4. Come, then, and join this holy group,
   And on to heaven go,
   To live in the beautiful land,
   Where joys forever are.

29 SATISFIED WITH JESUS

1. I am satisfied with Jesus,
   He has done so much for me,
   He has suffered to save me,
   He has died to make me free.

Chorus:
   I am satisfied, I am satisifed,
   I am satisfied with Jesus,
   But the question comes to me,
   When I think of Calvary,
   Is my Savior satisfied with me?

2. He is with me in my troubles,
   Best of friends of all is He;
   I can always depend on Jesus,
   Can He always depend on me?

3. I can hear the voice of Jesus
   Calling out and begging me,
   "Go and win the lost and sinning,"
   Is He satisfied with me?

4. When my work on earth is ended,
   And I go to heaven's home,
   Oh, that I could hear Him saying,
   "I am satisfied with you."

WHEREVER HE LEADS I'LL GO 30

(Jesus speaking)

1. "Carry your cross and follow Me,"
   I heard my Master say;
   "I gave My life to save you. Give up your all today."

Chorus:
   Wherever He leads I'll go,
   Wherever He leads I'll go,
   I'll follow my Christ Who loves me much,
   Wherever He leads I'll go.

2. He pulled me closer to His side,
   I wanted His wants to know,
   And in the wants I now will live,
   Wherever He leads I'll go.

3. My heart, my life, my all I bring,
   To Christ Who loves me true;
   He is my Master, Lord, and King,
   Wherever He leads I'll go.

31 TAKE TIME TO BE HOLY

1. Have time to be holy,
   Speak many times with your Lord;
   Stay close to Jesus always, and read His Bible.
   Make friends of God's saved people;
   Help people who are weak;
   Forgetting in nothing His blessing to seek.

2. Have time to be holy, the days pass on;
   Use much time in praying with Jesus alone—
   By praying to Jesus, same as Him you will be;
   Your friends in your actions His ways will see.

3. Have time to be holy, let Jesus be your Guide,
   And go not before Him, no matter what happens.
   In joy or in sorrow, still follow your Lord,
   And, praying to Jesus, still trust in His Word.

4. Have time to be holy, be calm in your soul;
   Each thought and each action beneath His control;
   And led by His Spirit to have much of love,
   You soon will be ready for living in heaven.

32 JESUS IS CALLING

1. Jesus is sweetly calling you home—
   Calling today, calling today;
   Why from the goodness of love will you leave
   Farther and farther away?

Chorus:
   Calling today, calling today,
   Jesus is calling, is sweetly calling today.

2. Jesus is calling the tired to rest—
   Calling today, calling today;
   Bring Him your burden and you will be blessed;
   He will not turn you away.

3. Jesus is waiting; O come to Him now—
   Waiting today, waiting today;
   Come with your sins; at His feet low bow;
   Come and no longer wait.

4. Jesus is begging; O listen to His voice:
   Hear Him today, hear Him today;
   All who believe on His name will be glad;
   Hurry arise and away.

O WHY NOT TONIGHT? 33

1. O do not let the Word leave,
   And close your eyes to the truth;
   Poor sinner harden not your heart,
   Be saved, O tonight.

Chorus:
   O why not tonight?
   O why not tonight?
   Will you be saved?
   Then why not tonight?

2. Tomorrow's sun may never rise
   To bless your long-fooled sight;
   This is the time, O then be wise,
   Be saved, O tonight.

3. Our Lord in love is waiting still,
   And will you now His love refuse?
   Give up right now your stubborn way,
   Be saved, O tonight.

4. Our blessed Lord refuses none
   Who want to Him their souls join;
   Believe on Him, the work is done,
   Be saved, O tonight.

34 I LOVE HIM

1. I have found a wonderful Friend
   Who is all the world to me.
   On the cross of Calvary
   He died to make me free.
   His name is Jesus, wonderful Jesus.
   He's the One Who is all the world to me.

Chorus:
   I love Him, because He first loved me.
   I love Him, because of Calvary.
   I will live for Him forever,
   And never sorry be.
   Yes, I love Him, because He first loved me.

35 RING THE BELLS OF HEAVEN

(Explanation needed)

1. Ring the bells of heaven! There is joy now,
   For a soul returning from sin.
   See! the Father meets him out upon the way,
   Welcoming His weary, wandering child.

Chorus:
   Glory! glory! how the angels sing;
   Glory! glory! how the loud harps ring!
   'Tis the saved people like a mighty sea,
   Sending out the song of the free.

2. Ring the bells of heaven! There is joy now,
   For the wanderer now is saved.
   Yes, a soul is saved from sinful way,
   And is born now a saved person.

3. Ring the bells of heaven! Send the news now.
   Angels sing the glad victory song!
   Tell the joyful story, tell it far places!
   For a precious soul is born again.

HAVE THINE OWN WAY, LORD 36

1. Have Your way, Lord, have Your way,
   You are the Maker, I am the clay.
   Mold me and make me, after Your will,
   While I am waiting, yielded and still.

2. Have Your way, Lord, have Your way.
   Search me and try me, Jesus, now.
   Whiter than snow, Lord, wash me just now,
   As before God, humbly I bow.

3. Have Your way, Lord, have Your way.
   Wounded and weary, help me I pray.
   Power all power, surely is Yours,
   Touch me and heal me, Savior divine!

4. Have Your way, Lord, have Your way.
   Keep over my body full stay.
   Fill with Your Spirit till all shall see
   Christ only, always living in me!

THEN JESUS CAME 37

1. One man sat alone near the highway begging,
   His eyes were blind, the light he could not see;
   He held his clothes and shivered in the dark,
   Then Jesus came and made the dark leave.

Chorus:
   When Jesus comes the Devil's power is broken,
   When Jesus comes the tears are dried away,
   He takes the sadness and fills the life with glory,
   Because all is changed when Jesus comes to stay.

2. So men today can find the Savior,
   They cannot win free from sin and temptation;
   Their broken hearts leave them sad and lonely,
   Then Jesus came and lived within man's heart.

38 ALMOST PERSUADED

1. "Almost decided" now to believe;
   "Almost decided" Christ to receive;
   Maybe now some soul to say,
   "Go, Spirit, go Your way.
   Some other better day
   On You I'll call."

2. "Almost decided," come, come today;
   "Almost decided," look not away;
   Jesus invites you here,
   Angels are waiting near,
   Prayers said from heart so dear,
   O sinner come.

3. "Almost decided," life now is past!
   "Almost decided," death comes at last!
   "Almost" is not enough;
   "Almost" is but to fail!
   Sad, sad, that awful cry,
   "Almost, but lost!"

39 LOOK AND LIVE

1. I have a story from the Lord, hallelujah!
   The story to you I will give;
   It is written in Jesus' Book, hallelujah!
   It is only that you "look and live."

Chorus:
   Look and live, my brother, live,
   Look to Jesus now and live;
   It is written in His Book, hallelujah
   It is only that you "look and live."

2. I have a story full of life, hallelujah!
   A story, O my friend, for you;
   It is a story from heaven, hallelujah!
   Jesus said it, so I know it is true.

WHEN WE ALL GET TO HEAVEN — 40

1. Sing the wonderful love of Jesus,
   Sing His mercy and His grace;
   In the houses above in heaven,
   He'll prepare for us a place.

Chorus:
   When we all arrive in heaven,
   What a day of rejoicing that will be!
   When we all see Jesus,
   We'll sing and shout the victory.

2. Let us all be true and faithful,
   Believing, serving every day.
   Only one look of Jesus in heaven,
   Will make the sorrows of life forgotten.

3. Onward to heaven before us.
   Soon Jesus' beauty we will see.
   Soon the beautiful gates will open,
   We will walk the streets of gold.

STEPPING IN THE LIGHT — 41

1. Trying to walk in the way of the Savior,
   Trying to follow our Savior and King;
   Building our lives by His wonderful example,
   Happy, how happy, the songs that we sing.

Chorus:
   How beautiful to walk in the way of the Savior,
   Walking in the light, walking in the light;
   How beautiful to walk in the way of the Savior,
   Led in paths of light.

2. Trying to walk in the way of the Savior,
   Upward, go upward, we will follow our Leader;
   When we shall see Him, "The King in His beauty,"
   Happy, how happy, our place at His side.

42 BLESSED ASSURANCE

1. Blessed to know, Jesus is mine!
   Oh, what a joy that heaven is mine!
   Son of salvation, bought by God,
   Born of His Spirit, washed in His blood.

Chorus:
   This is my story, this is my song,
   Praising my Savior all the day long;
   This is my story, this is my song,
   Praising my Savior all the day long.

2. Perfect obedience, perfect happiness,
   Thinking of heaven now comes to my mind;
   Angels come down and bring from heaven
   Actions of mercy, talking of love.

3. Perfect obedience, all is at rest,
   I in my Savior am happy and blessed;
   Watching and waiting, looking to heaven,
   Filled with His goodness, filled with His love.

43 GRACE GREATER THAN OUR SIN

1. Wonderful grace of our loving Lord
   Grace that is more than all of our sin,
   There on Calvary's mountain given,
   There where the blood of Jesus was given.

Chorus:
   Grace, grace, God's grace,
   Grace that forgives and cleans within;
   Grace, grace, God's grace,
   Grace that is greater than all our sin.

2. Wonderful, wonderful, perfect grace,
   Freely given to all who believe;
   You who are wanting to see God's face,
   Will you this minute His grace receive?

HEAVENLY SUNSHINE 44

1. Walking in sunlight, all of my life;
   In all the good times, and bad ones too;
   Jesus has said, "I'll never leave you,"
   Promise so wonderful that never can fail.

Chorus:
   Heavenly sunlight, heavenly sunlight,
   Filling my soul with glory divine;
   Hallelujah, I am rejoicing,
   Singing His praises, Jesus is mine.

2. In the bright sunlight, always rejoicing,
   Going my way to my home above;
   Singing His praises gladly I'm walking,
   Walking in sunlight, sunlight of love.

THERE IS POWER IN THE BLOOD 45

1. Will you be free from the burden of sin?
   There is power in the blood, power in the blood;
   Will you win a victory over sin?
   There is wonderful power in the blood [of Jesus].

Chorus:
   There is power, power, wonderful working power
   In the blood of Jesus;
   There is power, power, wonderful working power
   In the precious blood of Jesus.

2. Will you be free from your suffering and pride?
   There is power in the blood, power in the blood;
   Come for forgiveness to Calvary's blood;
   There's wonderful power in the blood.

3. Will you do service for Jesus your King?
   There is power in the blood, power in the blood;
   Will you live daily God's praises to sing?
   There's wonderful power in the blood.

46 JESUS PAID IT ALL

1. I hear the Savior say,
   "Your strength truly is small,
   Child of weakness, watch and pray,
   Find in Jesus your everything."

Chorus:
   Jesus paid it all,
   All to Him I owe,
   Sin had left an evil heart,
   Jesus washed it white as snow.

2. Lord, now truly I find
   Your power, and Yours alone,
   Can change the sin in me,
   And change my hard heart.

3. For nothing good have I
   Where by Your grace to take—
   I'll be saved from my sin
   By the blood of God's Son.

4. And when, before the throne,
   I stand in Jesus saved,
   "Jesus died my soul to save,"
   My lips will say.

47 SOFTLY AND TENDERLY

1. Quietly and kindly Jesus is calling;
   Calling for you and for me;
   See, up in heaven He's waiting and watching,
   Watching for you and for me.

Chorus:
   Come home, come home, you who are tired, come
      home;
   Truly, kindly, Jesus is calling,
   Calling, O sinner, come home!

2. Why should we wait when Jesus is begging,
   Begging for you and for me?
   Why should we wait and obey not His goodness,
   Goodness for you and for me?

3. Time is now fading, the minutes are passing,
   Passing from you and from me;
   Darkness is coming, deathbeds are coming,
   Coming for you and for me.

4. Oh! for the wonderful love He has promised,
   Promised for you and for me;
   Though we have sinned, He has mercy and
      forgiveness,
   Forgiveness for you and for me.

JESUS ALONE   48

1. Jesus alone can give salvation,
   And die in my place on the cross,
   Making me free from sin and sorrow,
   For time and eternity.

Chorus:
   I'm filled with joy
   Because I know He loves me,
   And satisfied that Jesus will never fail,
   No other person is same as Jesus,
   No one so near, No one so dear as He.

2. Good and kind was Jesus to save me,
   And take all my burden away,
   All of my sin He forgave me,
   And changed all my night to day.

3. Jesus alone can change my sadness,
   And give me a wonderful peace,
   Jesus alone can bring me gladness,
   And make all my worry stop.

49 NOTHING BUT THE BLOOD OF JESUS

1. What can wash away my sin?
   Nothing but the blood of Jesus;
   What can make me clean again?
   Nothing but the blood of Jesus.

Chorus:
   Oh! Wonderful is that blood,
   That makes me white same as snow;
   No other way I know,
   Nothing but the blood of Jesus.

2. For my forgiveness this I see,
   Nothing but the blood of Jesus;
   For my cleaning this I beg—
   Nothing but the blood of Jesus.

3. Nothing can pay for my sin,
   Nothing but the blood of Jesus;
   Nothing good that I have done,
   Nothing but the blood of Jesus.

4. This is all my hope and peace,
   Nothing but the blood of Jesus;
   This is all my right doing,
   Nothing but the blood of Jesus.

50 LET OTHERS SEE JESUS IN YOU

1. While passing through this world of sin,
   And others your life will see,
   Be clean and pure without, within,
   Let others see Jesus in you.

Chorus:
   Let others see Jesus in you,
   Let others see Jesus in you;
   Keep telling the story, be faithful and true,
   Let others see Jesus in you.

2. What joy 'twill be at end of life,
   In great houses beyond the sky,
   To find some souls that you have won;
   Let others see Jesus in you.

3. Then live for Christ both day and night,
   Be faithful, be brave and true,
   And lead the lost to life in heaven;
   Let others see Jesus in you.

4. Your life's same as book before their eyes,
   They read it again and again;
   Oh, does your life show them to Christ?
   Do others see Jesus in you?

NEAR TO THE HEART OF GOD   51

1. There is a place of quiet rest,
   Near to the heart of God,
   A place where sin cannot hurt me,
   Near to the heart of God.

Chorus:
   O Jesus, blessed Redeemer,
   Sent from the heart of God,
   Keep us, who wait before you,
   Near to the heart of God.

2. There is a place of comfort sweet,
   Near to the heart of God.
   A place where we our Savior meet,
   Near to the heart of God.

3. There is a place of full freedom,
   Near to the heart of God,
   A place where all is joy and peace,
   Near to the heart of God.

52 CONSTANTLY ABIDING

1. There's a peace in my heart that the world never gave,
   A peace it cannot take away [from me];
   Though the trials of life may surround like a cloud,
   I've a peace that has [finished] come there to stay.

Chorus:
   Constantly [always] abiding [staying near],
   Jesus is mine;
   Constantly [always] abiding [staying near],
   Rapture [inspiration] divine;
   He never leaves me lonely,
   Whispers, O so [much] kind:
   "I will never leave thee," Jesus is mine.

2. All the world seemed to sing of a Savior and King,
   When peace sweetly came to my heart;
   Troubles all fled away and my night turned [became] to
       day,
   Blessed Jesus, how glorious Thou art!

3. This treasure [gift] I have in a temple of body
   While here on His foot-stool [earth] I roam;
   But He's coming to take [carry] me some glorious day
   Over there to my heavenly home.

53 JESUS LOVES EVEN ME

1. I am so glad that our Father in heaven
   Tells of his love in the Book He has given;
   Wonderful things in the Bible I see:
   This is the dearest, that Jesus loves me.

Chorus:
   I am so glad that Jesus loves me,
   Jesus loves me, Jesus loves me,
   I am so glad that Jesus loves me,
   Jesus loves even me.

2. If I forget Him and wander away,
   Still He does love me wherever I go;
   Back to His dear loving arms would I run,
   When I remember that Jesus loves me.

3. Oh, if there's only one song I can sing,
   When in His beauty I see the great King,
   This shall my song in eternity be;
   "Oh, what a wonder that Jesus loves me."

WHOSOEVER WILL   54

1. "Whosoever heareth," shout, shout the sound!
   Spread the blessed good news all the world around;
   Tell the joyful news wherever man is living,
   "Whosoever will may come."

Chorus:
   "Whosoever will, whosoever will!"
   Send the good news over vale and hill;
   'Tis the loving Father calls the sinner home:
   "Whosoever will may come."

2. Whosoever cometh need not delay
   Now the door is open, enter while you may;
   Jesus is the true, the only Living Way:
   "Whosoever will may come."

3. "Whosoever will!" the promise is secure;
   "Whosoever will!" forever must endure;
   "Whosoever will!" 'tis life forever more;
   "Whosoever will may come."

55 HE LIVES

1. I serve a living Savior, He's in the world today,
   I know that He is living, no matter what men say;
   I see His hand of goodness,
   I hear His voice of cheer;
   And when I need Him, He's always near.

Chorus:
   Jesus lives, Jesus lives, Christ Jesus lives today!
   He walks with me and talks with me
   Along life's narrow road,
   He lives, He lives,
   Salvation gives to all.
   You ask me how I know He lives,
   He lives within my heart.

2. In all the world around me, I see His loving work,
   And if my heart becomes tired,
   I never will give up;
   I know that He is leading me
   Through all the trouble way
   The time of Jesus' coming will be very soon.

3. Rejoice, rejoice, O Christian,
   Now use your voice and sing,
   Eternal hallelujahs to Jesus Christ the King!
   The hope of all who seek Him,
   The help of all who find Him,
   None other is so loving, so good and sweet.

56 I KNOW I'LL SEE JESUS SOME DAY

1. Sweet is the hope that is happy in my soul—
   I know I'll see Jesus future day!
   Then what if the dark clouds of sin come over me?
   I know I'll see Jesus future day!

Chorus:
> I know I'll see Jesus future day!
> I know I'll see Jesus future day!
> What a joy it will be
> When Jesus' face I shall see,
> I know I'll see Jesus future day!

2. Though I must travel by faith, not by know,
   I know I'll see Jesus future day!
   No evil can harm me, no foe can scare me—
   I know I'll see Jesus future day!

3. Darkness is coming, but hope shines within,
   I know I'll see Jesus future day!
   What joy when He comes to rid every sin:
   I know I'll see Jesus future day!

YE MUST BE BORN AGAIN   57

1. A ruler one time came to Jesus at night
   To ask Him the way of salvation and right;
   Then Jesus told answer in words true and clear,
   "You must be born in heart."

Chorus:
> "You must be born in heart; You must be born in
>   heart;
> I truly, truly say to you, You must be born in heart."

2. O, you who want to go to that heavenly place
   And sing with the saved ones the song that will bless;
   The life everlasting if you want to have,
   "You must be born in heart."

3. A loved one in heaven your heart wants to see,
   At the beautiful gate may be watching for you;
   Then listen to the words that I will sing,
   "You must be born in heart."

58 WONDERFUL, WONDERFUL JESUS

1. There is never a day so lonely,
   There is never a night so long,
   But the soul that is trusting Jesus
   Will somewhere find a song.

Chorus:
   Wonderful, wonderful Jesus,
   In the heart He has given a song;
   A song of salvation, of bravery, of strength,
   In the heart He has given a song.

2. There is never a cross so heavy,
   There is never a burden of sadness,
   But that Jesus will help to carry
   Because He loves so much.

3. There is never a trouble or burden,
   There is never a sorrow or loss,
   But that Jesus in love will lighten
   When carried to the cross.

4. There is never a bad sinner,
   There is never a lost person,
   But that God can in mercy forgive
   Through Jesus Christ, His Son.

59 O HAPPY DAY

1. O happy day that made me decide
   On You, my Savior and my God!
   Now let this happy heart sing,
   And tell its happiness to all people.

Chorus:
   Happy day, happy day,
   When Jesus washed my sins away!
   He taught me how to watch and pray,
   And live rejoicing every day;
   Happy day, happy day,
   When Jesus washed my sins away.

2. O happy saved, that keeps my promise
   To Jesus Who have all my love!
   Let cheerful songs fill His heaven,
   While to that wonderful place I go.

3. Is finished, the great salvation is finished!
   I am my Lord's, and He is mine;
   He lifted me, and I followed Him,
   Wanting to confess the sin of mine.

4. Now rest, my long-troubled heart;
   Stay on this blessed rest;
   No never from my Lord depart,
   With Jesus every good will have.

THROW OUT THE LIFE-LINE 60

(Explanation needed)

1. Throw out the Life-Line across the dark wave,
   There is a brother whom some person should save;
   Some person's brother! O who then will try
   To throw out the Life-Line, his sin to save?

Chorus:
   Throw out the Life-Line! Throw out the Life-Line!
   Someone is drifting away; Throw out the Life-Line!
   Throw out the Life-Line! Someone is sinking today.

2. Throw out the Life-Line with hand quick and strong;
   Why do you tarry, why linger so long?
   See! Man is sinking, O hasten now
   And out with the Life Boat! away, then, away.

3. Short time the time to save be finished,
   Short time they go to eternity's shore;
   Haste then my brother, no time for delay,
   But throw out the Life-Line and save them today.

61 SEND THE LIGHT

1. There's a call comes ringing over the sinful way,
   Send the light! Send the light!
   There are souls to help, there are souls to save,
   Send the light! Send the light!

Chorus:
   Send the light! the blessed good news light;
   Let it shine from place to place!
   Send the light! the blessed good news light;
   Let it shine forevermore.

2. We have heard the heavenly call today,
   Send the light! Send the light!
   And a golden offering at the cross we lay,
   Send the light! Send the light!

3. Let us pray that grace may everywhere abound,
   Send the light! Send the light!
   And a Christlike spirit everywhere be found.
   Send the light! Send the light!

4. Let us not grow weary in the work of love,
   Send the light! Send the light!
   Let us win souls for a crown in heaven,
   Send the light! Send the light!

62 THE BANNER OF THE CROSS

1. There's a royal banner given for show,
   To the soldiers of the King;
   As a banner bright we lift it up now,
   While as saved people we sing.

Chorus:
   Marching on, marching on,
   For Christ count everything but loss!
   And to crown Jesus King, toil and sing,
   'Neath the banner of the cross!

2. Though the foe may fight and come as the flood,
   Let the banner be showed.
   And beneath the banner, same as soldiers of the Lord,
   For the truth will always stay!

3. Over land and sea, wherever man dwells,
   Make the good news known;
   Of the crimson banner now the story tell,
   While the Lord shall claim His saved people.

4. When the glory dawns 'tis coming very near,
   It is nearer day by day;
   Then before our King the foe shall disappear,
   And the cross the world shall stay.

THE LOVE OF GOD 63

1. The love of God is greater more,
   Than words or pen can tell;
   It goes beyond the highest star,
   And goes down to the lowest hell,
   The sinful too, bowed down with burdens,
   God gave His Son to win;
   His sinning child, He came to save,
   And forgave from his sin.

Chorus:
   Oh, love of God, how wonderful and clean!
   It has no end and it's strong! It will forevermore stay—
   The saved and angel's song.

2. If we could change all water to ink,
   And change the skies into paper,
   If we could change the grass to pens,
   And every man could write very good;
   To write the love of God above,
   Would use all the ink.
   And all the paper would not be enough
   Up there in the sky.

64 I WALK WITH THE KING

1. In sorrow I wandered, my spirit much burdened
   But now I am happy—now I can rest;
   From morning to evening happy, happy I sing,
   And this is the reason—I walk with the King.

Chorus:
   I walk with the King, hallelujah!
   I walk with the King, praise His name!
   No more I roam, my soul looks to heaven,
   I walk and I talk with the King.

2. For years in much sin I was bound,
   The world could not help me—no comfort I found;
   But now like the birds and the sunshine of spring,
   I'm free and happy—I walk with the King.

3. O soul full of sin in the life full of trouble,
   Look up and let Jesus come into your life;
   The joy of salvation to you He would give,
   Come into the sunlight and walk with the King.

65 ONE DAY

1. Past day when heaven was filled with His praises,
   Past day when sin was as black as could be;
   Jesus came down to be born of a virgin,
   Lived among men, my example is He.

Chorus:
   Living, Jesus loved me; dying, He saved me;
   Buried, He carried my sins far away;
   Rising, He freed from blame; Keeps me forever;
   Future day Jesus coming, oh, wonderful day!

2. Past day people led Jesus up Calvary's mountain,
   Past day people nailed Jesus to die on the cross;
   Suffering much, hated and refused;
   Bearing our sins, my Redeemer is Jesus!

3. Past day people left Jesus alone in the garden,
   Past day Jesus rested, from suffering free,
   Angels came down over Jesus' tomb to keep watch,
   Hope of the hopeless, my Savior is Jesus!

4. Past day the grave could not keep Jesus,
   Past day the stone rolled away from the door;
   Then Jesus arose, over death Jesus had conquered;
   Now is ascended, my Lord evermore!

5. Future day horns many will sound of Jesus' coming,
   Future day the skies with His glory will shine;
   Wonderful day, my beloved One bringing,
   Wonderful Jesus, this Savior is mine!

ONWARD, CHRISTIAN SOLDIERS   66

1. Onward, Christian soldiers, marching as to war,
   With the cross of Jesus going on before!
   Christ the royal Master, leads against the foe;
   Forward into battle, see His banners go.

Chorus:
   Onward, Christian soldiers, marching as to war,
   With the cross of Jesus going on before.

2. At the sight of victory, Satan's followers run;
   On now, Christian soldiers, on to victory!
   Hell's all places shiver at the shout of praise,
   People, use your voices, loud your words now sing!

3. The same as mighty army, moves the Christian people;
   People, we are walking where other people have
      walked;
   We are not divided; all one group are we,
   Together in hope and beliefs, together in love.

4. Onward, now you people, join our happy group,
   Sing with us all voices in the victor's song;
   Glory, praise, and honor, unto Christ the King:
   This through many, many years men and angels sing.

67 GLORY TO HIS NAME

1. Near at the cross where my Savior died,
   There for cleansing from sin I begged,
   There from my heart was the sin washed clean;
   Glory to His name.

Chorus:
   Glory to His name, glory to His name;
   There from my heart was the sin washed clean;
   Glory to His name.

2. I am so wondrously saved from sin,
   Jesus so sweetly lives within.
   There at the cross where Jesus saved me;
   Glory to His name.

3. Oh, wondrous Jesus Who saves from sin,
   I am so glad I have let Jesus in;
   There Jesus saves me and keeps me clean;
   Glory to His name.

4. Come to this Jesus so good and sweet;
   Give your bad soul to the Savior now;
   Be saved today and be made God's child;
   Glory to His name.

68 FACE TO FACE

1. Face to face with Christ my Savior,
   Face to face—what will it be—
   When with gladness I will see Him,
   Jesus Christ who died for me.

Chorus:
   Face to face I will see Jesus,
   Far beyond the star-filled sky;
   Face to face in all His glory,
   I shall see Him future glad day.

2. What happiness with my Jesus,
   When are finished grief and pain;
   When the sinful ways are ended,
   And the hard things will be known.

3. Face to face! O happy minute!
   Face to face—to see and know;
   Face to face with my Redeemer,
   Jesus Christ Who loves me so.

LIVING FOR JESUS 69

1. Living for Jesus a life that is true,
   Trying to please Him in all that I do,
   Giving obedience, glad hearted and free,
   This is the pathway of blessing for me.

Chorus:
   O Jesus, Lord and Savior, I give myself to You;
   For You, in Your death on the cross,
   Did give Yourself for me;
   I have no other Master, my heart will be Your home,
   My life I give, now to live,
   O Christ for You alone.

2. Living for Jesus, Who died in my place,
   Bearing on Calvary my sin and shame,
   Much love makes me answer His call,
   Follow His leading and give Him my all.

3. Living for Jesus wherever I am,
   Doing each duty in His holy name,
   I will suffer hurt or loss,
   Thinking each hard time a part of my life.

4. Living for Jesus through earth's little time,
   My loving gift is the sight of His smile,
   Seeking the lost people Jesus died to save,
   Bringing the tired people to find rest in Him.

70 I AM THINE, O LORD

1. I am Yours, O Lord, I have heard Your voice,
   And it told Your love to me;
   But I want to be in the arms of God
   And be nearer, nearer to God.

Chorus:
   Bring me nearer, nearer blessed Lord,
   To the cross where You have died;
   Bring me nearer, nearer, nearer blessed Lord,
   To Your precious bleeding side.

2. Use me now to Your work, Lord
   By the power of grace divine;
   Let my soul look up with staying hope,
   And my way be joined in God.

3. Oh, the wonderful delight of a single hour
   That before God's throne I spend,
   When I kneel in prayer, and with You, my God,
   I talk as friend with friend!

4. There is much love that I cannot know
   Till I cross over into heaven;
   There is much joy that I can't arrive
   Till I rest in peace with God.

71 WHERE HE LEADS ME

1. I can hear my Savior calling,
   I can hear my Savior calling,
   I can hear my Savior calling,
   "Take your cross and follow, follow Me."

Chorus:
   Where He leads me I will follow,
   Where He leads me I will follow,
   Where He leads me I will follow,
   I'll go with Him, with Him all the way.

2. I'll go with Him through the garden,
   I'll go with Him through the garden,
   I'll go with Him through the garden,
   I'll go with Him, with Him all the way.

3. I'll go with Him through the judgment,
   I'll go with Him through the judgment,
   I'll go with Him through the judgment,
   I'll go with Him, with Him all the way.

4. He will give me grace and glory,
   He will give me grace and glory,
   He will give me grace and glory,
   And go with me, with me all the way.

MUST JESUS BEAR THE CROSS ALONE?　　72

1. Must Jesus carry the cross alone,
   And all the people become free?
   No; have a cross for every person
   And have a cross for me.

2. The blessed, holy cross I'll carry
   Till death will make me free,
   And then go to heaven my crown to have
   For there is a crown for me.

3. Upon the golden street and near
   Jesus' pierced feet,
   Joyful, I'll give my golden crown,
   And His sweet name say again.

4. O wondrous cross! O glorious crown!
   O going to heaven day!
   You angels, from the stars come down,
   And carry my soul to heaven.

73 HAVE FAITH IN GOD

1. Have faith in God when your lifeway is lonely,
   He sees and knows all the way you have come.
   Never alone are the smallest of His children;
   Have faith in God, have faith in God.

Chorus:
   Have faith in God, God is on His throne;
   Have faith in God, God watches over His people;
   God cannot fail, He must rule all [people].
   Have faith in God, have faith in God.

2. Have faith in God when your prayers are not
      answered,
   Your every prayer He will never forget;
   Wait on the Lord, trust His Word and be patient;
   Have faith in God, He'll answer you.

3. Have faith in God in your pain and your sorrow,
   His heart is touched with your sadness and hurt;
   Give all your troubles and your burdens to Jesus,
   And leave troubles there, oh, leave troubles there.

4. Have faith in God when all others fail around you;
   Have faith in God, He give for His own;
   God cannot fail—if all worlds will perish,
   God rules, He's Boss upon His throne.

74 IN THE GARDEN

1. I come to the flower place alone,
   While the rain is still on the flowers,
   And the voice I hear, coming to my ear,
   The Son of God I know.

Chorus:
   And Jesus walks with me, and He talks with me,
   And He tells me I am His child;
   And the joy we have as we stay together
   None other person has ever known.

2. Jesus speaks, and the sound of His voice
   Is much sweet the birds stop their singing,
   And the melody that Jesus gave to me,
   Within my heart is singing.

3. I stay in the flower place with Jesus
   But the night around me is coming,
   But He tells me go through the voice of sad
   His voice to me is calling.

COUNT YOUR BLESSINGS   75

1. When upon life's way you are full of trouble,
   When you are disappointed, thinking all is lost,
   Count your many blessings, say them one by one,
   And it will surprise you what the Lord has given.

Chorus:
   Count your blessings, say them one by one;
   Count your blessings, see what God has given;
   Count your blessings, say them one by one;
   Count your many blessings, see what God has given.

2. Are you ever burdened with much trouble?
   Does the burden seem heavy you are asked to carry?
   Count your many blessings, every doubt will leave,
   And you will be singing as the days pass by.

3. When you look at others with their lands and gold,
   Think that Christ has promised you His wealth much;
   Count your many blessings, money cannot buy
   Your pay in heaven, nor your home on high.

4. So, amid the trouble, maybe great or small,
   Do not be disappointed, God is over all;
   Count your many blessings, angels will see,
   Help and comfort give you to your journey's end.

76 'TIS SO SWEET

1. Is much sweet to trust in Jesus,
   And to believe His every word;
   And to rest on all His promises,
   And to know what says the Lord.

Chorus:
   Jesus, Jesus, how I trust Him,
   How He's helped me over and over!
   Jesus, Jesus, wonderful Jesus!
   O for grace to trust Him more!

2. O much sweet to trust in Jesus,
   And to trust His cleansing blood;
   And with little faith to save me
   With the healing, cleansing blood!

3. Yes, 'tis sweet to trust in Jesus,
   And from sin and wrong to finish;
   And from Jesus only taking
   Life and rest, and joy and peace.

4. I'm much glad I learned to trust Jesus,
   Wonderful Jesus, Savior, Friend;
   And I know that You are with me,
   Will be with me when I die.

77 WONDERFUL WORDS OF LIFE

1. Sing words again and again to me,
   Wonderful words of life.
   Let me more of the beauty see,
   Wonderful words of life.
   Words of life and beauty,
   Teach me faith and duty.

Chorus:
   Beautiful words, wonderful words,
   Wonderful words of life.
   Beautiful words, wonderful words,
   Wonderful words of life.

2. Christ the blessed Person, gives to all people,
   Wonderful words of life,
   Sinner people, listen to the loving words,
   Wonderful words of life.
   Salvation is freely given,
   Carrying us to heaven.

3. Sweetly tell that Jesus saves,
   Wonderful words of life;
   Giving forgiveness and peace to all,
   Wonderful words of life.
   Jesus, only Savior,
   Save me forever.

AM I A SOLDIER OF THE CROSS?   78

1. Am I a soldier of the cross,
   A follower of the Son,
   And shall I fear to own His way,
   Or blush to speak His name?

2. Must I be carried to the skies
   On flowery beds of ease,
   While others fought to win the prize,
   And sailed through bloody seas?

3. Are there no foes for me to meet,
   Must I not fight the flood?
   Is this vile world a friend to grace,
   To help me on to God?

4. Sure I must fight, if I would win,
   Increase my courage, Lord;
   I'll do the toil, endure the pain,
   Supported by Thy Word.

79 TELL ME THE OLD, OLD STORY

1. Tell me the old, old story, of not seen things above,
   Of Jesus and His glory, of Jesus and His love;
   Tell me the story easy, same as to a little child,
   For I am weak and tired, need help for full sin.

Chorus:
Tell me the old, old, story, tell me the old, old story,
Tell me the old, old story of Jesus and His love.

2. Tell me the story slowly, that I can remember it—
   That wonderful salvation, God's way to destroy sin;
   Tell me the story often, for I forget very soon,
   You tell me in the morning and I forget by noon.

3. Tell me the story softly, with earnest talk and truth,
   Remember I'm the sinner whom Jesus came to save;
   Tell me the story always, if you would really be,
   In any time of trouble, a helper to me.

4. Tell me the same old story, when you have reason
      to fear
   That this world's short good times are costing me
      too much;
   Yes, and when that world glory, good time is coming
      in my heart,
   Tell me the old, old story: "Christ Jesus saved
      your soul."

80 OH, HOW I LOVE JESUS

1. There is a name I love to hear,
   I love to sing its praise;
   It is the same as music to me,
   The sweetest name on earth.

Chorus:
Oh, how I love Jesus,
Oh, how I love Jesus,

Oh, how I love Jesus,
Because He first loved me.

2. It tells me about a Savior's love,
   Who died to make me free;
   It tells of His wondrous blood,
   The sinner's perfect prayer.

3. It tells of One Whose loving heart
   Can feel my worst sorrow,
   Who in every sorrow bears a part,
   That no one can bear on earth.

NOTHING BETWEEN 81

1. Nothing between my soul, and the Savior
   Naught of this world's foolish dream;
   I have given up all sinful play,
   Jesus is mine, there's nothing between.

Chorus:
   Nothing between my soul and the Savior,
   So that His blessed face may be seen;
   Nothing preventing the least of His favor,
   Keep the way clear! Let nothing between.

2. Nothing between like worldly play time;
   Habits of like, though harmless they seem,
   Must not my heart from Jesus be separated,
   Jesus is my all, there's nothing between.

3. Nothing between, like pride or boasting;
   Self or friends shall not between;
   Though it may cost me much trouble,
   I am decided, there's nothing between.

4. Nothing between, maybe many hard trials,
   The whole world against me come;
   Watching with prayer and much self give up,
   I'll win at last, with nothing between.

82 TAKE THE NAME OF JESUS WITH YOU

1. Take the name of Jesus with you,
   Person of sorrow and much sad;
   It will joy and comfort give you,
   Take it then wherever you go.

Chorus:
   Loving name, O how sweet!
   Hope of earth and joy of heaven;
   Loving name, O how sweet:
   Hope of earth and joy of heaven.

2. Take the name of Jesus always
   As a protection from every sin;
   If temptations come around you,
   Say that holy name in prayer.

3. O the loving name of Jesus!
   How it thrills our souls with joy.
   When His loving arms receive us,
   And His songs we will sing!

4. At the name of Jesus bowing,
   Falling down at His feet,
   King of kings in heaven we'll crown Him,
   When our life on earth is done.

83 I AM RESOLVED

1. I have decided no more to wait,
   Filled by the world's pleasure
   Things that are higher, things that are honor,
   These things have gotten my sight.

Chorus:
   I will hurry to Jesus,
   Hurry much glad and free,
   Jesus, greatest, highest,
   I will come to Thee.

2. I have decided to go to the Savior,
   Leaving my sin and strife;
   Jesus is the true One, Jesus is the just One,
   He has the words of life.

3. I have decided to follow the Savior,
   Faithful and true each day.
   Hear what Jesus says, do what Jesus wants,
   He is the Living Way.

4. I have decided and who will go with me?
   Come friends, do not wait,
   Taught by the Bible, led by the Spirit,
   We'll walk the heavenly way.

HE'S A WONDERFUL SAVIOR TO ME   84

1. I was lost in sin, but Jesus saved me;
   He's a wonderful Savior to me;
   I was bound by fear, but Jesus made me free;
   He's a wonderful Savior to me.

Chorus:
   For He's a wonderful Savior to me,
   He's a wonderful Savior to me;
   I was lost in sin, but Jesus saved me;
   He's a wonderful Savior to me.

2. He's a Friend stay true, much patient and much kind;
   He's a wonderful Savior to me;
   Everything I need in Him I can find;
   He's a wonderful Savior to me.

3. Sweeter grows the love of Jesus day by day;
   He's a wonderful Savior to me;
   Sweeter is His grace while going on my way;
   He's a wonderful Savior to me.

85 CLOSE TO THEE

1. You, my everlasting Savior
   More than friend or life to me;
   All along my earthly journey,
   Savior, let me walk with You.
   Close to You, close to You,
   Close to You, close to You;
   All along my earthly journey,
   Savior, let me walk with You.

2. Not for ease or worldly pleasure,
   Not for fame my prayer will be;
   Gladly will I work and suffer,
   Only let me walk with You.
   Close to You, close to You,
   Close to You, close to You;
   Gladly will I work and suffer,
   Only let me walk with You.

3. Lead me through the time of death,
   Carry me over to heaven's land;
   Then the gate of life eternal
   Will I go through, Lord, with You.
   Close to You, close to You,
   Close to You, close to You;
   Then the gate of life eternal
   Will I go through, Lord, with You.

86 SAVED, SAVED!

1. I've found a Friend Who is all to me,
   His love is always true;
   I love to tell how He saved me
   And what His love can do for you.

Chorus:
   Saved by His power divine, saved to new life
      much fine!
   Life now is sweet and my joy is very full,
   For I'm saved, saved, saved!

2. He saves me from every sin and hurt,
   He keeps my soul each day;
   I'm depending much on His mighty love;
   I know He'll guide me all the way.

3. When poor and in need and all alone,
   In love Jesus said to me,
   "Come to Me and I'll lead you to heaven,
   To live with Me eternally."

WHEN THE MORNING COMES   87

1. Troubles are all around,
   And we cannot understand
   All the ways that God would lead us
   To that blessed promised heaven;
   But He'll guide us all the way,
   And we'll follow till we die;
   We will understand it better in the future.

Chorus:
   In the future, when the Savior comes,
   When the saved of God are gathered home,
   We will tell the story how we've been saved;
   We will understand it better in the future.

2. Often our plans have failed,
   Disappointments have come,
   And we have walked in sorrow,
   Sad hearted and alone;
   But we're trusting in the Lord,
   And it says in His Word,
   We will understand it better in the future.

3. Temptations, hidden troubles,
   Many times surprise us,
   And our hearts are made to hurt
   For some careless word or act,
   And we wonder why the trouble
   When we try to do our best,
   But we'll understand it better in the future.

88 NOW I BELONG TO JESUS

1. Jesus, my Lord, will love me forever,
   No power of sin can separate me from Him,
   He gave His life to save my soul,
   Now I belong to Him.

Chorus:
   Now I belong to Jesus, Jesus belongs to me,
   Not for the years of time alone, but for eternity.

2. One time I was lost in sin's deep,
   Jesus came down to bring me salvation;
   Lifted me up from sorrow and shame,
   Now I belong to Him.

3. Joy floods my soul because Jesus has saved me,
   Freed me from sin that long had enslaved me.
   His wonderful blood He gave to save,
   Now I belong to Him.

89 THE LIGHT OF THE WORLD IS JESUS

1. The whole world was lost in the darkness of sin.
   The Light of the world is Jesus.
   Like sunshine at noonday Jesus' glory shone in,
   The Light of the world is Jesus.

Chorus:
   Come to the Light, 'tis shining for you.
   Sweetly the Light, came upon me.
   Once I was blind, but now I can see:
   The Light of the world is Jesus.

2. No darkness have we who in Jesus abide,
   The Light of the world is Jesus.
   We walk in the Light when we follow our Guide,
   The Light of the world is Jesus.

3. You live in darkness with sin-blinded eyes,
   The Light of the world is Jesus;
   Go, wash at Jesus' asking, and light will arise,
   The Light of the world is Jesus.

4. No need of the sunlight in heaven we need.
   The Light of the world is Jesus.
   The Son is the Light in the City of Gold,
   The Light of the world is Jesus.

WHEN I SEE THE BLOOD   90

(Explanation needed)

1. Christ our Redeemer died on the cross
   Died for the sinner, paid all his due;
   All who receive Jesus need never fear
   Yes, Jesus will pass, will pass over you.

Chorus:
   When I see the blood, when I see the blood,
   When I see the blood, I will pass, I will pass over you.

2. Leader of sinners, Jesus can save,
   As He has promised, so will He do;
   Oh, sinner, hear Jesus, trust in His Word
   Then Jesus will pass, will pass over you.

3. Judgment is coming, all people will be there,
   Each person receiving what he earned;
   Hide in the saving sin-cleansing blood
   And Jesus will pass, will pass over you.

4. Oh, what love, oh, much love!
   Jesus has power, Jesus is true;
   All who believe are safe from the storm,
   Oh, Jesus will pass, will pass over you.

91 AT CALVARY

1. Many years I stayed in sin and pride,
   Not caring that my Lord was crucified,
   Not knowing that it was for me He died,
   At Calvary.

Chorus:
   Love was wonderful and grace was free,
   Forgiveness there was given much to me,
   There my burdened soul found freedom,
   At Calvary.

2. Oh, the love that made salvation's plan!
   Oh, the grace that brought it down to man!
   Oh, the wonderful way that God will save
   At Calvary.

3. Now I have given to Jesus everything,
   Now I gladly have Him as my King,
   Now my happy soul can only sing
   Of Calvary.

92 WHY DO YOU WAIT?

1. Why do you wait, dear brother,
   Oh, why do you wait so long?
   Your Savior is waiting to give you
   A place in His heavenly home.

Chorus:
   Why not? why not?
   Why not come to Him now?
   Why not? why not?
   Why not come to Him now?

2. What do you hope, dear brother,
   To get by longer waiting?
   There's no one to save you but Jesus,
   There's no other way but His way.

3. Do you not feel, dear brother,
   His Spirit now working within?
   Oh, why not accept His salvation,
   And give up your burden of sin?

4. Why do you wait, dear brother?
   The time is fast passing away;
   Your Savior is wanting to bless you,
   There's danger and death in waiting.

THERE IS A FOUNTAIN*   93

1. There is a cross filled with blood
   Coming from Jesus' body;
   And sinners under that blood lose all their fill of sin;
   Lose all their fill of sin, lose all their fill of sin,
   And sinners under that blood lose all their fill of sin.

2. The dying thief happy to see that blood in his day;
   And now may I, full sin same as thief,
   Wash all my sins away;
   Wash all my sins away; wash all my sins away;
   And now may I full sin same as thief,
   Wash all my sins away.

3. Now in a better, sweeter song,
   I'll sing His power to save,
   When my poor, can't sing tongue lies silent in the
       grave;
   Lies silent in the grave; lies silent in the grave.
   When this poor, can't sing tongue lies silent in the
       grave.

---

*This song is full of symbolic and figurative language. Before singing the
song, explain that this song is about Jesus' dying on the cross and the
blood He shed for us that we might have everlasting life.

94 CHRIST RETURNETH

1. May be morning time, when the day is awaking,
   When sunlight through darkness and shadow is
       coming,
   That Jesus will come in the fullness of glory,
   To receive from the world saved people.

Chorus:
   O Lord Jesus, how long, how long
   Till we shout the glad song,
   Christ returns! Hallelujah!
   Hallelujah! Amen!
   Hallelujah! Amen.

2. It may be at midday, it may be at twilight,
   It may be perhaps that the blackness of midnight
   Will burst in light in the fullness of His glory,
   When Jesus receives saved people.

3. While all with Jesus cry hallelujah,
   From heaven descending,
   With glorified saints and the angels also,
   With grace on Jesus' brow, like a halo of glory,
   Will Jesus receive "His child."

4. Oh, joy, oh wonderful, maybe we go without dying,
   No sickness, no sadness, no fear, and no crying,
   Caught up in the clouds, with our Lord in glory,
   When Jesus receives saved people.

95 BLESSED REDEEMER

1. Up Calvary's mountain one sad morning,
   Walked Christ my Savior, very much tired;
   In place of sinners death on the cross,
   That He might save them from going to hell.

Chorus:
   Blessed Redeemer! precious Redeemer!
   I imagine I see Him on Calvary's cross;

Hurting and bleeding, for sinners praying—
Sinners won't listen—He's dying for me!

2. "Father, forgive them!" that's what He prayed,
   While all His life-blood flowed from His side;
   Praying for sinners while in much pain—
   No one but Jesus could have loved much.

3. O how I love Him, Savior and Friend,
   How can my praises stay to the end:
   Through many years on heaven's land,
   My words will praise Him forevermore.

WHAT A FRIEND WE HAVE IN JESUS 96

1. What a Friend we have in Jesus,
   All our sins and griefs He bears!
   What an honor to tell
   Everything to God in prayer!
   O what peace we often don't have,
   O what pain we need not bear,
   All because we do not tell
   Everything to God in prayer!

2. Have we hard times and temptations?
   Is there trouble anywhere?
   We should never give up,
   Tell it to the Lord in prayer.
   Can we find a friend so faithful
   Who will all our sorrows bear?
   Jesus knows our every weakness,
   Tell it to the Lord in prayer.

3. Are we weak and much burdened,
   Burdened with a load of trouble?
   Wonderful Savior, still our helper,
   Tell it to the Lord in prayer.
   Do your friends hate and leave you?
   Tell it to the Lord in prayer;
   With His love He'll keep and protect you,
   You will find peace there.

97 MY REDEEMER

1. I will sing of my Redeemer
   And His wondrous love to me;
   On the cruel cross He suffered,
   From all sin to make me free.

Chorus:
   Sing, oh, sing of my Redeemer,
   With His blood He saved me,
   On the cross He bore my sin,
   Paid the debt and made me free.

2. I will tell the wondrous story,
   How my lost heart to save,
   In His no-end love and mercy,
   He the pay freely gave.

3. I will praise my dear Redeemer,
   His winning power I'll tell,
   How the victory He gives
   Over sin, and death, and hell.

4. I will sing of my Redeemer,
   And His heavenly love to me;
   He from death to life has brought me,
   Son of God, with Him to be.

98 JESUS SAVES!

1. We have heard the joyful sound:
   Jesus saves! Jesus saves!
   Tell the story all around:
   Jesus saves! Jesus saves!
   Take the news to every place,
   Climb the mountains and cross the waters;
   "Onward!" is our Lord's command:
   Jesus saves! Jesus saves!

2. Give the winds a strong voice,
   Jesus saves! Jesus saves!
   Let the nations now rejoice,

Jesus saves! Jesus saves!
Shout salvation full and free;
Highest hills and deepest caves;
This our song of victory,
Jesus saves! Jesus saves!

MEET ME THERE   99

1. In the happy golden place [heaven].
   There the faithful leave no more,
   When the troubles of life are finished,
   Meet me there [in heaven];
   There the night have gone away
   Into sweet and perfect day,
   I am going home to stay,
   Meet me there [in heaven].

Chorus:
   Meet me there, meet me there,
   There the tree of life is growing.
   Meet me there.
   When the troubles of life are finished,
   In the happy golden place [heaven],
   There the faithful leave no more.
   Meet me there.

2. Here our best hopes are nothing,
   Things we love broken to two;
   But in heaven no hurt or pain.
   Meet me there;
   By the river very bright in the city full of joy;
   There our faith is lost in sight.
   Meet me there.

3. There the music of angels I hear,
   And saved people forever sing
   In the palace of the King,
   Meet me there;
   When the sweet meeting join heart to heart
   And friend to friend;
   In a world that never shall end,
   Meet me there.

100 BRING THEM IN

(Explanation needed)

1. Listen to the Shepherd's voice I hear,
   Out in the dry place dark and bad,
   Calling the sheep who've gone astray,
   Far from the Shepherd's home.

Chorus:
   Bring people in, bring people in,
   Bring people in from the place of sin;
   Bring people in, bring people in,
   Bring the wandering people to Jesus.

2. Who'll go and help the Shepherd?
   Help Him the wandering people to find?
   Who'll bring the lost people to Jesus,
   Where they'll be kept from sin?

3. Out in the dry place hear people cry,
   Out on the mountains far and high;
   Listen! 'tis Jesus tells you,
   "Go find the sheep wherever they be."

101 I KNOW THAT MY REDEEMER LIVETH

1. I know that my Redeemer lives,
   And on the earth again will stand;
   I know eternal life He gives,
   That grace and power are in His hand.

Chorus:
   I know, I know that Jesus lives,
   And on the earth again will stand;
   I know, I know that life He gives,
   That grace and power are in His hand.

2. I know His promise never fails,
   The word He speaks, it cannot die;
   Though awful death my body will have,
   Still I will see Him future day.

3. I know my great home He builds,
   That where He is there I will be;
   O wondrous thought, for me He loves,
   And He at last will come for me.

GOD BE WITH YOU   102

1. God be with you till we meet again,
   By His sayings guide, keep you,
   With His saved ones safely keep you;
   God be with you till we meet again.

Chorus:
   Till we meet, till we meet;
   Till we meet at Jesus' feet;
   Till we meet, till we meet,
   God be with you till we meet again.

2. God be with you till we meet again,
   'Neath His arms protecting hide you,
   Daily food give you;
   God be with you till we meet again.

3. God be with you till we meet again;
   When life's trouble much around you,
   Feel Jesus' arms around you;
   God be with you till we meet again.

4. God be with you till we meet again;
   Keep love's banner round you;
   Finish death coming to you;
   God be with you till we meet again.

103 MY FAITH LOOKS UP TO THEE

1. My faith looks up to God,
   You Son of Calvary,
   Savior divine!
   Now hear me while I pray,
   Take all my sin away,
   O let me from this day
   Be wholly Yours.

2. May God's rich grace to me,
   Give strength to my weak heart,
   My wants improve,
   As Jesus has died for me,
   O may my love to You,
   Pure, warm, and never change
   A living fire!

3. While life's dark way I walk,
   And griefs around me come,
   Jesus be my guide;
   Change darkness into today,
   Wipe sorrow's tears away,
   Nor let me ever stray
   From Jesus' side.

4. When ends life's foolish dream,
   When death's cold comes to me,
   And o'er me roll;
   Blessed Savior, then, in love,
   Fear and distrust remove;
   O bear me safe above,
   A saved person.

104 I KNOW WHOM I HAVE BELIEVED

1. I know not why God's wonderful grace
   To me God has made known,
   Or why I not good—Christ in love
   Saved me for Himself.

Chorus:
> But I know Who I have believed,
> And am decided that God can
> Keep that which I have given
> To God waiting for the day.

2. I know not how God's saving faith
    To me He did give,
    Or how believing in Jesus' Word
    Brought peace within my heart.

3. I know not when my Lord will come,
    Maybe night or noon-day time,
    Or if I walk this life with Him,
    Or "meet Jesus in the clouds."

IN THE CROSS OF CHRIST 105

1. In the cross of Christ I glory,
    Covering over the sin of time,
    All the night of holy story
    Gathers round the cross glorious.

2. When the troubles of life come on me,
    No hope nor fears bother me,
    Never shall the cross leave me,
    Now it glows with peace and joy.

3. When the sun of blessing is shining,
    Light and love upon my way,
    From the cross the light shining,
    Adds more bright to the day.

4. Suffering and blessing, pain and pleasure,
    By the cross are made clean,
    Peace is there that knows no measure,
    Joys that through all time abide.

106 AT THE CROSS

1. O yes, and did my Savior bleed?
   And did my Ruler die?
   Did Jesus die upon the cross
   For sinners bad like me?

Chorus:
   At the cross, at the cross
   Where I first knew the truth,
   And the burden of my heart went away,
   It was there by faith I received Jesus,
   And now I am happy all the day!

2. Was it for sins that I have done,
   He died upon the cross?
   Surprising sorrow! Grace not known,
   And love more than we know!

3. Well, yes, the sun in darkness hid,
   And covered Jesus there,
   When Christ, the Mighty Maker, died
   For man and all his sin.

4. But tears of grief can never give again
   The much love that I owe:
   Here Lord, I give myself to You,
   'Tis all that I can do!

107 GOD WILL TAKE CARE OF YOU

1. Be not worried what can happen,
   God will keep you;
   Beneath His arms of love stay,
   God will keep you.

Chorus:
   God will keep you,
   Through every day, going all the way;
   He will keep you,
   God will keep you.

2. Through days of work when you are tired,
   God will keep you.
   When great dangers in your path will come,
   God will keep you.

3. All you may need God will give,
   God will keep you.
   Everything you ask God will give,
   God will keep you.

4. No matter what will be the trouble,
   God will keep you.
   Weary person, lean upon Jesus,
   God will keep you.

AMAZING GRACE 108

1. Surprising grace! how sweet to hear,
   That saved a sinner same as me!
   I one time was lost, but now am saved,
   Was dumb, but now I know.

2. Truly grace that taught my heart to fear,
   And grace my fears stopped;
   How wonderful that grace did look
   The hour I first believed!

3. Through many dangers, works, and fears,
   I have finished arrived;
   'Tis grace that brought me safe in life,
   And grace will lead me to heaven.

4. When we've been in heaven ten thousand years,
   Bright shining as the sun,
   We will have many days to sing God's praise
   Same as when we first began.

109 ARE YOU WASHED IN THE BLOOD?

(Explanation needed)

1. Have you been to Jesus for the cleansing power?
   Are you washed in the blood of Jesus?
   Are you fully trusting in Jesus' grace this hour?
   Are you washed in the blood of Jesus?

Chorus:
   Are you washed in the blood,
   In the soul-cleansing blood of Jesus?
   Is your soul clean? Are you white as snow?
   Are you washed in the blood of Jesus?

2. Are you walking daily by the Savior's side?
   Are you washed in the blood of Jesus?
   Do you rest each moment in the Crucified?
   Are you washed in the blood of Jesus?

3. When Jesus comes
   Will your robes be white?
   Are you washed in the blood of Jesus?
   Will your soul be ready for the houses bright,
   And be washed in the blood of Jesus?

4. Finish with the heart that is full of sin,
   And be washed in the blood of Jesus;
   There's a cleaning power for the soul not clean,
   O be washed in the blood of Jesus.

110 I GAVE MY LIFE FOR THEE

(Jesus talking)

1. I gave My life for you,
   My wondrous blood I gave,
   That you could saved be,
   And raised up from the dead;
   I gave, I gave My life for you,
   What have you given for Me?
   I gave, I gave My life for you,
   What have you given for Me?

2. My Father's house of joy,
   My glory circled throne,
   I left for earthly sadness,
   For wanderings sad and lone;
   I left, I left it all for you,
   Have you left anything for Me?
   I left, I left it all for you,
   Have you left anything for Me?

3. I suffered much for you,
   More than your signs can tell,
   Of awful pain and hurt,
   To save you from hell;
   I've suffered, I've suffered it all for you,
   What have you suffered for Me?
   I've suffered, I've suffered it all for you,
   What have you suffered for Me?

I AM PRAYING FOR YOU   111

1. I have a Savior, He's living in heaven,
   A sweet, loving Savior, but earth-friends are few;
   And now He is watching in much love over me,
   And, oh, that my Savior was your Savior, too.

Chorus:
   For you I am praying, for you I am praying,
   For you I am praying, I'm praying for you.

2. I have a Father; to me He has given
   A hope for eternity, blessed and true;
   And soon will He call me to meet Him in heaven,
   But, oh, that He'd let me bring you with me, too!

3. When Jesus has found you, tell others the story,
   That my loving Savior is your Savior, too;
   Then pray that your Savior may bring them to heaven,
   And prayer will be answered—'Twas answered for
      you!

112 JUST AS I AM

1. Only as I am, with not one good,
   But that Your blood was given for me,
   And that You ask me come to You,
   O, Son of God, I come! I come!

2. Only as I am, and waiting not
   To take from my soul the one dark sin,
   To You whose blood can cleanse each sin,
   O Son of God, I come! I come!

3. Only as I am—all mixed up
   With many a trouble, many a doubt,
   Fightings and fears within, without,
   O Son of God, I come! I come!

4. Only as I am—poor, sinful, dumb;
   Saved, riches, knowing in the mind,
   Yes, all I need in You to find,
   O Son of God, I come! I come!

5. Only as I am—You will receive,
   Will welcome, forgive, cleanse, give rest,
   Because Your promise I believe,
   O Son of God I come! I come!

113 WHEN THE ROLL IS CALLED UP YONDER

1. When the trumpet of the Lord will blow,
   And time will be no more,
   And the morning comes, eternal bright and pretty;
   When the saved of earth will meet over in heaven,
   And the names are called in heaven,
   I will be there.

Chorus:
   When the names are called in heaven,
   When the names are called in heaven,

When the names are called in heaven,
When the names are called in heaven
I will be there.

2. Let us work for the Master from the
Morning till setting sun,
Let us talk of all His wondrous love and keep;
Then when all of life is finished,
And our work on earth is finished,
And the names are called in heaven,
I will be there.

TAKE MY LIFE AND LET IT BE 114

1. Take my life and let it be
Working, Lord, for You,
Take my hands and let them work,
At the call of Your love.

Chorus:
Lord, I give my life to You,
Yours forevermore to be,
Lord, I give my life to You.
Yours forevermore to be.

2. Take my feet, and let them be
Swift and beautiful for You.
Take my voice, and let me sing,
Always, only for my King.

3. Take my silver and my gold,
Not a little bit would I keep;
Take my moments and my days,
Let them stay in forever praise.

4. Take my way and make it Yours,
It shall be no more mine,
Take my heart, it is Your own,
It shall be Your royal throne.

115 NEARER, MY GOD, TO THEE

1. Nearer, my God, to You, nearer to You.
   Even though it be a cross that raises me;
   Still all my song shall be nearer, my God, to You,
   Nearer, my God, to You, nearer to You.

2. Though like the wanderer, the sun gone down,
   Darkness be over me, my rest is gone.
   Yet in my dreams I'd be nearer, my God, to You,
   Nearer, my God, to You, nearer to You.

3. There let the way become, steps into heaven;
   All that You sendest me, in mercy given:
   Angels to beckon me nearer, my God, to You,
   Nearer, my God, to You, nearer to You.

4. Then with my waking thoughts bright with Thy praise,
   Out of my much griefs, heaven I see,
   So by my troubles to be nearer, my God to You,
   Nearer, my God, to You, nearer to You.

5. Or if on joyful way, up through the sky,
   Sun, moon, and stars behind, up, up I go,
   Still all my song shall be, nearer my God to You,
   Nearer, my God, to You, nearer to You!

116 NAILED TO THE CROSS

1. There was One Who was wanting to die in my place,
   That a soul much sinful could live,
   And the path to the cross He was wanting to walk,
   All the sins of my life to forgive.

Chorus:
   My sins are nailed to the cross,
   Sin nailed to the cross,
   O how much Jesus did suffer!
   With much pain and loss,
   Jesus went to the cross!
   But He carried my sins with Him there [on cross].

2. He is kind and loving and patient with me,
   While He cleanses my heart of its sin;
   But no sending to hell, I know I am free,
   For my sins are all nailed to the cross.

3. I will hold to my Savior and never leave—
   I will joyfully live each day,
   With a song on my lips and a song in my heart,
   That my sins have been taken away.

THE NAME OF JESUS 117

1. The name of Jesus is much sweet,
   I love the name to say again;
   It makes my joys full and satisfied,
   The wonderful name of Jesus.

Chorus:
   "Jesus," O how sweet the name!
   "Jesus," every day the same;
   "Jesus," let all saved people say
   His lovely name forever.

2. I love the name of Jesus whose heart
   Knows all my griefs and bears much.
   Jesus tells all my fears to go—
   I love the name of Jesus.

3. That name I truly love to hear,
   It never fails my heart to cheer;
   The music stops the falling tears;
   O praise the name of Jesus.

4. No word of man can ever tell
   How sweet the name I love so much;
   Oh, let the praises ever be,
   Oh, praise the name of Jesus.

118 MORE LOVE TO THEE

1. More love to Jesus, O Christ, more love to You.
   Hear You the prayer I make on bended knee;
   This is my earnest prayer,
   More love, O Christ, to You,
   More love to You, more love to You.

2. Once earthly joy I wanted, sought peace and rest;
   Now Jesus alone I seek, give what is best;
   This all my prayer shall be,
   More love, O Christ, to You,
   More love to You, more love to You.

3. When sorrow does its work, giving grief and pain;
   Sweet are Your angels, sweet their song;
   When they can sing with me,
   More love, O Christ, to You,
   More love to You, more love to You!

4. Then shall my latest breath whisper Thy praise,
   This be the parting cry my heart shall raise;
   This still its prayer shall be;
   More love, O Christ, to You,
   More love to You, more love to You.

119 STANDING ON THE PROMISES

1. Trusting in the promises of Christ my King,
   Through eternal years let His praises be;
   Glory in the highest, I will shout and sing,
   Trusting in the promises of God.

Chorus:
   Trusting, trusting, trusting in the promises
      of God, my Savior;
   Trusting, trusting, I'm trusting in the promises of God.

2. Trusting in the promises that cannot fail,
   When I have much of doubt and fear in me,
   By the Bible, Word of God, I will have victory,
   Trusting in the promises of God.

3. Trusting in the promises of Christ the Lord,
   Joined to Him eternally by love so strong,
   Defeating sin daily with the Spirit's power,
   Trusting in the promises of God.

4. Trusting in the promises I cannot fall,
   Listening every minute to the Spirit's call,
   Resting in my Savior as my all in all,
   Trusting in the promises of God.

CHRIST AROSE   120

1. Dead in the grave Jesus lay—
   Jesus my Savior!
   Waiting the future day—
   Jesus my Lord!

Chorus:
   Up from the grave He arose,
   With a great victory over enemies;
   He arose a Victor from the dark grave,
   And He lives forever with the saved to rule.
   He arose! He arose! Hallelujah! Christ arose!

2. Proudly people watch His grave—
   Jesus my Savior!
   Proudly people shut the grave—
   Jesus my Lord!

3. Death cannot keep my Lord—
   Jesus my Savior!
   He rose up from the dead—
   Jesus my Lord!

1. Maybe not on the mountaintop,
   Or in the stormy sea;
   Maybe not at the war place,
   My Lord will have need of me;
   But if quiet, small voice of Jesus
   I hear telling me to go where it's new;
   I will say I will go with God near my side;
   I will go where God wants me to go.

Chorus:
   I will go where You want me to go, dear Lord,
   On mountain, or land, or sea;
   I will say what You want me to say, dear Lord,
   I will be what you want me to be.

2. Maybe today there are good words
   That Jesus would want me to say;
   And maybe now in the ways of sin,
   Some person I need seek,
   O, Savior, if You will lead me,
   Maybe dark and bad the way,
   My voice will tell the story sweet,
   I will say what You want me to say.

3. There's truly somewhere a poor place
   In earth's unsaved people so many
   Where I may work through life's short time
   For Jesus, the crucified.
   So, giving my all unto Your care,
   I know You love me!
   I'll do Your will with a heart true,
   I'll be what You want me to be.

MY JESUS, I LOVE THEE 122

1. My Jesus, I love You, I know You are mine,
   For You all the foolishness of sin I give up;
   My wonderful Savior, my Jesus are You;
   If I will love You, my Jesus, 'tis now.

2. I love You, because You have first loved me,
   And paid for my salvation on Calvary's cross;
   I love You for wearing the thorns on Your head;
   If I will love You, my Jesus, 'tis now.

3. I'll love You in life, I will love You in death,
   And praise You as long as You give me breath;
   And say when the death-sweat is cold on my head,
   If I will love You, my Jesus, 'tis now.

4. In houses of glory and no-end of joy;
   I'll always love You in heaven so bright;
   I'll win with the shining crown on my head,
   If I will love You, my Jesus, 'tis now.

REVIVE US AGAIN 123

1. We praise You, O God! For the Son of Your love,
   For Jesus Who died, and is now gone to heaven.

Chorus:
   Hallelujah! Yours the glory, hallelujah! Amen;
   Hallelujah! Yours the glory, make new us again.

2. We praise You, O God! For Your Spirit of light!
   Who has shown us our Savior, and made go our night.

3. All glory and praise to God's Son that was slain,
   Who has borne all our sins and has cleansed every sin.

4. Make new us again; fill each heart with Your love;
   Let each soul be filled again from heaven.

124 PASS ME NOT

1. Pass me not, O gentle Savior, hear my humble cry;
   While on others You are calling, do not pass me by.

Chorus:
   Savior, Savior, hear my humble cry;
   While on others You are calling, do not pass me by.

2. Let me at the throne of mercy find a sweet peace;
   Kneeling there in deep sorrow, help me to believe.

3. Trusting only in Your goodness, will I seek Your face.
   Save my hurt and broken spirit, save me by Your
      grace.

4. You the reason of all my comfort, more than life to me,
   Who have I on earth but You? Who in heaven but You?

125 MORE ABOUT JESUS

1. More about Jesus let me know,
   More of His grace to others show,
   More of His saving fullness see,
   More of His love Who died for me.

Chorus:
   More, more about Jesus,
   More, more about Jesus,
   More of His saving fullness see,
   More of His love Who died for me.

2. More about Jesus let me learn,
   More of His holy wants to know,
   Spirit of God, my teacher be,
   Showing the things of Christ to me.

3. More about Jesus on His throne,
   Riches in glory all His own;
   More of His people will be saved;
   More of His coming, Prince of Peace.

SINCE I HAVE BEEN REDEEMED 126

1. I have a song I love to sing,
   Because I have been redeemed,
   Of my Redeemer, Savior, King,
   Because I have been redeemed.

Chorus:
   Because I have been redeemed,
   Because I have been redeemed,
   I will glory in Jesus' name;
   Because I have been redeemed,
   I will glory in my Savior's name.

2. I have a Christ that satisfies,
   Because I have been redeemed:
   To do His will my highest prize,
   Because I have been redeemed.

3. I have good news, bright and clear,
   Because I have been redeemed,
   Gone every doubt and fear,
   Because I have been redeemed.

4. I have a home prepared for me,
   Because I have been redeemed,
   Where I shall dwell eternally,
   Because I have been redeemed.

127 ABIDE WITH ME

1. Stay with me: fast comes the end of life;
   The death comes nearer; Lord, with me stay:
   When other helpers fail, and comforts leave,
   Helper of the weak person, O, please stay with me!

2. Fast to end life's short time;
   Earth's joys are few, its glories fade away;
   Change and death in all around I see:
   O, God, Who changes not, please stay with me!

3. I need You near me every passing hour:
   What but Your grace can stop the tempter's power?
   Who same as Yourself my guide and help can be?
   Through sorrow and joy, O please stay with me!

4. Hold You the Bible before my closing eyes;
   Shine through the sadness, and show me to heaven:
   Heaven's morning comes, and earth's life is leaving—
   In life, in death, O Lord, please stay with me!

128 JESUS LOVES ME

1. Jesus loves me! this I know,
   For the Bible tells me true;
   Little children to Him are joined,
   They are weak, but God is strong.

Chorus:
   Yes, Jesus loves me,
   Yes, Jesus loves me,
   Yes, Jesus, loves me,
   The Bible tells me true.

2. Jesus loves me! He Who died
   Heaven's gates to open wide!
   He will take away my sin,
   Let His little child in heaven.

3. Jesus loves me! He will stay
   Close beside me all the way;
   If I love Him when I die,
   He will carry me home to heaven.

THE HAVEN OF REST

(Explanation needed)

1. My soul in sad exile was out on life's sea,
   So burdened with sin and distressed,
   Till I heard a sweet voice saying,
   "Make Me your choice,"
   And I entered the "Haven of Rest."

Chorus:
   I've joined my soul in the "Haven of Rest,"
   I'll sail the wild seas not again;
   The tempest may sweep over the wild stormy deep,
   In Jesus I'm safe evermore.

2. I yielded myself to Jesus' tender embrace,
   And, faith taking hold of the Word,
   My fetters fell off, and I joined my soul;
   The "Haven of Rest" is my Lord.

3. The song of my soul, since the Lord made me whole,
   Has been the old story so blessed,
   Of Jesus, Who will save whosoever will have
   A home in the "Haven of Rest."

4. How precious the thought that we all may rest,
   Like John the beloved and blessed,
   On Jesus' strong arm, where no trouble can harm,
   Secure in the "Haven of Rest."

5. Oh, come to the Savior, He patiently waits,
   To save by His power divine;
   Come join your soul in the "Haven of Rest,"
   And say, "My beloved Jesus is mine."

130 NO ONE EVER CARED FOR ME LIKE JESUS

1. I would like to tell you what I think of Jesus,
   Because I found in Him a friend so strong and true;
   I would tell you how He changed all my life,
   Jesus did something that no other friend could do.

Chorus:
No other person loved me same as Jesus,
There is no other friend so good as He;
No other person could take the sin and darkness
   from me,
O how much Jesus loved me.

2. My life was full of sin when Jesus found me,
   My heart was full of trouble and sad;
   Jesus put His strong arms of love around me,
   And He led me to go in the right way.

3. Every day Jesus helps me know I am saved,
   More and more I understand His words of love;
   Here I never know why Jesus came to save me,
   I will know when I see Jesus' face in heaven.

131 BRINGING IN THE SHEAVES

1. Going in the morning, going with kindness,
   Going in the noon time and the evening time,
   Waiting for the saved people, and the time of saving,
   We shall come rejoicing, bringing in the saved people.

Chorus:
Bringing in the saved people,
Bringing in the saved people,
We shall come rejoicing,
Bringing in the saved people;
Bringing in the saved people,
Bringing in the saved people,
We shall come rejoicing,
Bringing in the saved people.

2. Going in the sunshine, going in the shadows,
   Fearing neither clouds nor winter's chilling breeze;
   Future and future, many people saved,
   We shall come rejoicing, bringing in the saved people.

3. Going forth with weeping, going for the Savior,
   Though the many people not saved our spirit often
      grieves;
   When our weeping's over, Jesus will tell us welcome,
   We shall come rejoicing, bringing in the saved people.

THE OLD RUGGED CROSS 132

1. On a hill far away stood an old, old cross,
   The picture of suffering and shame;
   And I love that old cross
   Where the dearest and best Person
   For a world of lost sinners was killed.

Chorus:
   So I will love the old, old cross
   Till my life here on earth I will leave;
   I will trust the old, old cross
   And change it some day for a crown.

2. Oh, that old, old cross, so hated by the world,
   Has a wondrous meaning to me;
   For the dear Son of God left His glory in heaven,
   To bring cross to dark Calvary.

3. In the old, old cross, covered with blood so divine,
   A wondrous beauty I see;
   For 'twas on that old cross Jesus suffered and died,
   To forgive and save me.

4. To the old, old cross I will ever be true,
   Its shame and blame gladly bear,
   Then He'll call me future day to my home far away,
   Where His glory forever I'll share.

133 SINCE JESUS CAME INTO MY HEART

1. What a wonderful change in my life has been made
   Because Jesus came into my heart!
   I have joy in my soul for which long I have searched
   Because Jesus came into my heart!

Chorus:
   Because Jesus came into my heart,
   Because Jesus came into my heart,
   Much joy in my soul same as the sea waves roll,
   Because Jesus came into my heart.

2. I have stopped from my wandering and going in sin
   Because Jesus came into my heart;
   And my sins that were many are all washed away
   Because Jesus came into my heart!

3. I will go there to live in heaven I know
   Because Jesus came into my heart;
   And I'm happy, so happy as onward I go,
   Because Jesus came into my heart!

134 OUR BEST

1. Hear you the Savior's call, "Give Jesus your best!"
   For, be it big or small, that is His test.
   Do now the best you can, not for a prize,
   Not for the praise of man, but for the Lord.

Chorus:
   Every work for Jesus will be blessed,
   But He asks from every person his best.
   Our works may be few, these may be small,
   But unto Jesus we must give our best, our all.

2. Wait not for men to praise, notice not their ignore;
   Having the smile of God will give its joy!
   Helping the good and true never goes unblessed,
   All that we think or do, be it the best.

3. Death soon comes in a hurry, life gone fast;
   Workman and work must have test from heaven.
   Oh, want we in that day find rest, sweet rest,
   Which God has promised all who do their best.

WE'RE MARCHING TO ZION 135

1. Come we that love the Lord,
   And let our joys be known,
   Join in a song with sweet voice,
   Join in a song with sweet voice,
   And then go around the throne,
   And then go around the throne.

Chorus:
   We are marching to heaven,
   Beautiful, beautiful heaven,
   We are marching upward to heaven,
   The beautiful city of God.

2. Let people refuse [won't] sing,
   Who never knew our God,
   But children of the heavenly King,
   But children of the heavenly King,
   Can sing their joys to other people,
   Can sing their joys to other people.

3. The hill of heaven gives a thousand sacred sweets,
   Before we reach the heavenly place,
   Before we reach the heavenly place,
   Or walk the golden streets,
   Or walk the golden streets.

4. Then let our songs be heard
   And every tear be dry;
   We are marching through Jesus' place,
   We are marching through Jesus' place;
   To beautiful homes in heaven,
   To beautiful homes in heaven.

136 I'LL LIVE FOR HIM

1. My life, my love I give to Jesus,
   The Son of God Who died for me;
   Oh, may I always faithful be,
   My Savior and my God!

Chorus:
   I'll live for Him Who died for me,
   How happy then my life will be!
   I'll live for Him Who died for me,
   My Savior and my God!

2. O Jesus Who died on Calvary,
   To save my soul and make me free,
   I'll give all of my life to You,
   My Savior and my God.

137 JESUS IS ALL THE WORLD TO ME

1. Jesus is all the world to me,
   My life, my joy, my everything.
   He is my strength from day to day,
   Without Jesus I would sin;
   When I am sad, to Him I go,
   No other person can cheer me much.
   When I am sad, He makes me glad,
   Jesus is my Friend.

2. Jesus is all the world to me,
   My Friend when trials much;
   I go to Jesus for blessings, and
   Jesus gives them over and over.
   Jesus sends the sunshine and the rain,
   He sends the harvest's golden grain,
   Sunshine and rain, harvest of grain,
   Jesus is my Friend.

3. Jesus is all the world to me,
   And true to Jesus I'll stay.
   O how could I this Friend leave,

When Jesus much true to me?
Following Jesus I know I'm right,
Jesus watches over me day and night.
Following Jesus by day and night,
Jesus is my Friend.

4. Jesus is all the world to me,
   I have no better friend.
   I trust Him now,
   I will trust Him when life's
   Many days will end;
   Beautiful life with Jesus, Friend,
   Beautiful life that has no end.
   Eternal life! Eternal joy!
   Jesus is my Friend.

LEANING ON THE EVERLASTING ARMS 138

1. What a fellowship, what a joy divine,
   Leaning on the everlasting Jesus;
   What a blessedness, what a peace is mine,
   Leaning on the everlasting Jesus.

Chorus:
   Leaning, leaning, safe and stay from all trouble;
   Leaning, leaning, leaning on the everlasting Jesus.

2. Oh, how sweet to walk in this traveling way,
   Leaning on the everlasting Jesus;
   Oh how bright the path grows from day to day,
   Leaning on the everlasting Jesus.

3. What have I to worry, what have I to fear,
   Leaning on the everlasting Jesus;
   I have blessed peace with my Lord very near,
   Leaning on the everlasting Jesus.

139 NEAR THE CROSS

1. Jesus keep me near the cross,
   There a precious fountain
   Free to all, the saving blood
   Flows from Calvary's mountain.

Chorus:
   In the cross, in the cross,
   Be my glory ever,
   Till my raptured soul shall find
   Rest beyond in heaven.

2. Near the cross, a trembling soul,
   Love and mercy found me.
   There the bright and morning Star
   Shed its beams around me.

3. Near the cross, O Son of God,
   Show its pictures to me.
   Help me walk from day to day,
   With its shadows o'er me.

4. Near the cross I'll watch and wait,
   Hoping, trusting ever,
   Till I reach the golden place
   Just up in heaven.

140 THERE SHALL BE SHOWERS OF BLESSING

1. There shall be many, many blessings:
   This is the promise of God;
   There shall be times of making new,
   Come from the Savior in heaven.

Chorus:
   Many, many blessings,
   Many blessings we need
   Mercy blessings round us are coming,
   But for the blessings we plead.

2. There shall be many, many blessings,
   Precious reviving again;
   Over the hills and the valleys,
   Sound of abundance of blessings.

3. There shall be many, many blessings;
   Send them upon us, O Lord;
   Give to us now renewing,
   Come and now honor Thy Word.

4. There shall be many, many blessings:
   Oh, that today they might come,
   Now as to God we're confessing,
   Now as on Jesus we call.

I LOVE HIM   141

1. Gone from my heart the sin and all its joy;
   Gone are my sins and all that would scare;
   Gone all time, and by His grace I know
   The wondrous blood of Jesus cleanses white as snow.

Chorus:
   I love Him, I love Him,
   Because He first loved me.
   And paid for my salvation on
   Calvary's cross.

2. One time I was lost deep in the life of sin;
   One time was a slave to doubts and fears within;
   One time was afraid to trust a loving God,
   But now my sin is washed away in Jesus' blood.

3. One time I was bound, but now I am made free;
   One time I was dumb, but now the truth I know;
   One time I was dead, but now in Christ I live,
   To tell the world the peace that He alone can give.

142 HIS WAY WITH THEE

1. Will you live for Jesus, and be always true and good?
   Will you walk with Him within the narrow road?
   Will you have Him bear your burden, carry all
      your load?
   Let Him have His way with you.

Chorus:
   His power can make you what you should be;
   His blood can cleanse your heart and make you free;
   His love can fill your soul and you will see
   It was best for Him to have His way with you.

2. Will you have Him make you free,
   And follow at His call?
   Will you know the peace that comes by giving all?
   Would you have Him save you, so that you can never
      fall?
   Let Him have His way with you.

3. Will you in His kingdom find a place of all time rest?
   Will you prove Him true in time of test?
   Will you in His service work always at your best?
   Let Him have His way with you.

143 SWEET BY AND BY

1. There's a place that is prettier than day,
   And by faith we can see it afar;
   For the Father waits over in heaven,
   To prepare us a living place there.

Chorus:
   In the sweet by and by, [future, future]
   We will meet in that beautiful land;
   In the sweet by and by, [future, future]
   We will meet in that beautiful land.

2. We will sing on that beautiful land
   The beautiful songs of the saved,

And our spirits will sorrow no more,
Not a frown for the blessing of rest.

3. To our rich Father above,
   We will give a gift of praise,
   For the glorious gift of His love,
   And the blessings that come in our lives.

LOVE LIFTED ME   144

1. I was living full of sin,
   Far from the peace of God,
   Very much sin was within,
   Dying to live no more;
   But the Master of all life
   Heard my begging prayer,
   From the sin He lifted me,
   Now saved am I.

Chorus:
   Love lifted me! Love lifted me!
   When nothing else could help, love lifted me.
   Love lifted me! Love lifted me!
   When nothing else could help, love lifted me.

2. All my heart to Him I give,
   Always to Him I'll stay,
   With His blessed self I'll live,
   Always His praises sing.
   Love so strong and so true
   Should have my soul's best songs;
   Faithful, loving service, too,
   To Him I give.

3. Souls in sin now look above,
   Jesus fully saves;
   He will lift you by His love
   Out of the awful sins.
   He's the Master of all things,
   Seas His wants obey;
   He your Savior wants to be—
   Be saved today.

145 REDEEMED

1. Saved—How I love to tell it!
   Saved by the blood of Jesus;
   Saved through His wonderful mercy,
   His child, and forever, I am.

Chorus:
   Saved, saved, saved by the blood of Jesus;
   Saved, saved, His child forever I am.

2. Saved and much happy in Jesus,
   No words my happy can tell;
   I know that the light of Him near me,
   With me will stay all the time.

3. I know I shall see in His beauty
   The King in Whose law I love;
   Who lovingly keeps my footsteps,
   And gives me songs in the night.

146 TELL ME THE STORY OF JESUS

1. Tell me the story of Jesus,
   Tell to my heart every word;
   Tell me the story most wonderful,
   Sweetest that any person has heard.
   Tell how the angels, together,
   Sang as they welcomed His birth,
   "Glory to God in the heavens!"
   Peace and good news to earth!

Chorus:
   Tell me the story of Jesus,
   Tell to my heart every word:
   Tell me the story most wonderful,
   Sweetest that any person has heard.

2. Nothing to eat in the desert,
   Tell of the days that are past,
   How for our sins Jesus was tempted,
   But was the winner at last.
   Tell of the years of His working,
   Tell of the sorrow He had;
   Jesus was hated and hurt,
   No home, not wanted and poor.

3. Tell of the cross where they killed Jesus,
   Suffering in tears and pain;
   Tell of the grave where they buried Jesus,
   Tell how Jesus lives again.
   Love in that story much tender,
   Clearer than before I see:
   Wait, let me cry while you tell me,
   Love paid the sin-debt for me.

I AM AMAZED   147

1. I feel surprised that God can love me,
   So full of sin, so covered with shame;
   Make me to walk with Jesus Who is above me,
   Cleaned by the power of Jesus' saving name.

Chorus:
   I feel surprised that God can always save me,
   Nothing but the cross could take away my sin;
   Through faith in Christ eternal life He gave me,
   Now Jesus lives forever within.

2. I feel surprised that God can always bless me,
   Make me His child and give me Jesus' grace;
   For all is perfect and Jesus will keep me,
   Jesus has kept for all who seek His face.

148 I SURRENDER ALL

1. All to Jesus I give,
   All to Him I freely give;
   I will always love and trust Him,
   Always near Him daily live.

Chorus:
   I give all, I give all;
   All to You, my blessed Savior,
   I give all.

2. All to Jesus I give,
   Humbly at His feet I bow;
   Worldly joys are all forgotten,
   Take me Jesus, take me now.

3. All to Jesus, I give,
   Make me, Savior, all Yours;
   Let me feel the Holy Spirit,
   Truly know that you are mine.

4. All to Jesus I give,
   Lord, I give myself to You;
   Fill me with Your love and power,
   Let Your blessing come on me.

149 OTHERS

1. Lord, help me live from day to day
   In much a self-forgetful way
   That when I kneel to pray
   My prayer will be for others.

Chorus:
   Others, Lord, yes, others,
   Let this my way be,
   Help me to live for others,
   That I may live as You.

2. Help me in all the work I do
   To always be honest and true

And know that all I'd do for You
Must needs be done for others.

3. And when my work on earth is done,
   And my new work in heaven is begun,
   May I forget the crown I've won,
   While thinking still of others.

SUNLIGHT   150

1. I wandered in the shades of night,
   Till Jesus came to me,
   And with the sunlight of His love
   Makes all my darkness flee.

Chorus:
   Sunlight, sunlight in my soul today,
   Sunlight, sunlight, all along the way;
   Since the Savior found me, took away my sin,
   I have had the sunlight of His love within.

2. Though clouds may gather in the sky,
   And billows round me roll,
   However dark the world may be,
   I've sunlight in my soul.

3. While walking in the light of God,
   I sweet talk find;
   I press with holy walking on,
   And leave the world behind.

4. I cross the wide, wide fields,
   I journey over the plain,
   And in the sunlight of Jesus' love,
   I reap the golden pay.

5. Soon I shall see Him as He is,
   The light that came to me.
   Behold the brightness of His face,
   Throughout eternity.

151 TELL IT TO JESUS

1. Are you tired, are you brokenhearted?
   Tell it to Jesus; tell it to Jesus;
   Are you crying because joys are gone?
   Tell it to Jesus alone.

Chorus:
   Tell it to Jesus; tell it to Jesus,
   He is the Friend you know best;
   You have no other such a friend or brother,
   Tell it to Jesus alone.

2. Do you fear the coming of sorrow?
   Tell it to Jesus; tell it to Jesus;
   Are you worried what will be tomorrow?
   Tell it to Jesus alone.

3. Are you troubled when you think of dying?
   Tell it to Jesus; tell it to Jesus;
   For Christ's coming Kingdom are you wanting?
   Tell it to Jesus alone.

152 I WILL SING THE WONDROUS STORY

1. I will sing the wonderful story
   Of the Christ Who died for me,
   How Jesus left His home in heaven,
   For the cross of Calvary.

Chorus:
   Yes, I'll sing the wonderful story
   Of the Christ Who died for me,
   Sing it with the Christians in heaven,
   Meeting in the beautiful heaven.

2. I was lost but Jesus found me,
   Found the person who went away,
   Have His loving arms around me.
   Led me back again follow Jesus.

3. I was hurt, but Jesus healed me,
   Faint was I from many a fall,
   Sight was gone, and fears possessed me,
   But Jesus freed me from all sin.

4. Days of sorrow still come to me,
   Sorrow's ways I many times have,
   But the Savior still is with me,
   By His hand I'm always led.

5. He will keep me till my life,
   Here on earth is completed,
   Then Jesus carry me to heaven,
   Where my loved ones I will meet.

O, THAT WILL BE GLORY   153

1. When all my labors and trials are finished
   And I arrive in that beautiful place,
   Only to be near the dear Lord I adore,
   Will through the years be glory for me.

Chorus:
   O, that will be glory for me,
   Glory for me, glory for me;
   When by His grace I shall look on His face,
   That will be glory, be glory for me.

2. When by the gift of His wonderful grace,
   I am given in heaven a place,
   Only to be there and to look on His face,
   Will through the years be glory for me.

3. Friends will be there I have loved long ago;
   Joy like a river around me will flow;
   But, only a smile from my Savior, I know,
   Will through the years be glory for me.

154 BLESSED BE THE NAME

1. O for a thousand tongues to sing,
   Blessed be the name of the Lord.
   The glories of my God and King,
   Blessed be the name of the Lord.

Chorus:
   Blessed be the name, blessed be the name,
   Blessed be the name of the Lord.
   Blessed be the name, blessed be the name,
   Blessed be the name of the Lord.

2. Jesus, the name that stops our fears,
   Blessed be the name of the Lord.
   'Tis music in the sinner's ears,
   Blessed be the name of the Lord.

3. Jesus breaks the power of sin,
   Blessed be the name of the Lord.
   Jesus' blood can make the sinner clean,
   Blessed be the name of the Lord.

155 I WOULD BE LIKE JESUS

1. Sinful good times try to call me;
   I would be like Jesus;
   Nothing sinful shall get me.
   I would be like Jesus.

Chorus:
   Be like Jesus, this my song,
   In the home and in the town;
   Be like Jesus, all day long!
   I would be like Jesus.

2. He has broken every sin,
   I would be like Jesus;
   That my soul may serve Him better,
   I would be like Jesus.

3. All the way from earth to heaven,
   I would be like Jesus;
   Telling again and again the story,
   I would be like Jesus.

4. That in heaven He may meet me,
   I would be like Jesus;
   Hear His Word, "Good work" say to me,
   I would be like Jesus.

SWEET PEACE, THE GIFT OF GOD'S LOVE 156

1. There comes to my heart one sweet song,
   A glad and an exciting song;
   I sing it again and again,
   Sweet peace, the gift of God's love.

Chorus:
   Peace, peace, sweet peace!
   Wonderful gift from above!
   Oh, wonderful, wonderful peace!
   Sweet peace, the gift of God's love!

2. Through Christ on the cross peace was made,
   My sin by His death was destroyed;
   No other person can give
   Sweet peace the gift of God's love.

3. With Jesus for peace I live,
   And when I keep close to Jesus,
   There is nothing but peace that comes,
   Sweet peace, the gift of God's love.

ALL BECAUSE OF CALVARY

   All my sins are gone, all because of Calvary.
   Life is filled with song, all because of Calvary.
   Christ my Savior died, died from sin to make me free.
   Future day He's coming, oh, wondrous, glorious day.
   All, yes, all because of Calvary.

157 DON'T GO AWAY WITHOUT JESUS

Don't go away without Jesus,
Don't go away without Him.
For He suffered on Calvary to save you
And cleanse from your heart every sin.
Make your decision for Jesus,
Let Him come into your heart.
Make sure right now of salvation,
Do not without Him leave.

158 WHAT IF IT WERE TODAY?

1. Jesus is coming to earth again,
What if it happened today?
Coming in power and love to rule,
What if it were today?
Coming to take the saved to heaven,
All who are saved and free from sin,
On all the earth who are every city
What if it happened today?

Chorus:
Glory, glory, joy to my heart will bring,
Glory, glory, when we shall crown Jesus King.
Glory, glory, hurry to prepare the way,
Glory, glory, Jesus is coming future day.

2. Devil's power will then be finished
O that it were today!
Sorrow and sickness shall be no more,
O that it were today!
Then shall the dead in Christ arise,
Caught up to meet Jesus in the skies,
When shall these glories meet our eyes?
What if it happened today?

3. Faithful and true will God find us here,
If Jesus maybe come today?
Sorrow and crying will be no more,
O Jesus come today!

Then will the dead in Christ arise,
And go to meet Jesus in heaven,
Watch for Jesus coming—happy day,
What if it happened today?

ALL THE WAY MY SAVIOR LEADS ME
159

1. All the way my Savior leads me;
   What other thing have I to ask?
   Can I doubt His kind mercy,
   Who through life has been my guide?
   Heavenly peace, divine comfort,
   Here by faith in Jesus to live!
   For I know, what will happen to me,
   Jesus does all things right.
   For I know, what will happen to me,
   Jesus does all things right.

2. All the way my Savior leads me,
   Cheers each winding path I walk,
   Gives me grace for every trouble,
   Gives me everlasting life.
   When my tired steps may falter,
   And my soul has a need.
   Coming from Jesus near me,
   Yes! Much joy I see;
   Coming from Jesus near me,
   Yes! Much joy I see.

3. All the way my Savior leads me;
   Oh, the fullness of His love!
   Perfect rest to me is promised
   In my Father's house above.
   When my spirit, up in heaven,
   Go the way to heaven above,
   This my song through endless time:
   Jesus led me all the way;
   This my song through endless time:
   Jesus led me all the way.

II. CHORUSES

A, B, C SONG 1

A, B, C, D, E, F, G: Jesus died for you and me.
H, I, J, K, L, M, N; Jesus died for sinful men.
O, P, Q, R, S, T, U; I believe God's Word is true.
U, V, W; God has promised you
X, Y, Z; A home eternally.

Z, Y, X, and W, V; God is watching you and me.
U, T, S, R, Q, P, O; Jesus loves me, this I know.
N, M, L, K, J, and I; I will meet Him in the sky.
H, G, F, E; God has promised me,
D, C, B, A; I'll be with Him some day.

I LOVE HIM 2

I love Jesus, I love Jesus,
Because He first loved me.
And purchased my salvation on Calvary.

SOME DAY 3

Some day I shall be like Jesus, some day like Him.
Changed to His heavenly beauty when His face I see.
Some day I shall be like Jesus, some day like Him.
Hallelujah, that wonderful promise He gave to me.

GOD'S WORD CAN NEVER FAIL 4

God's Word can never fail, never fail, never fail;
God's Word can never fail. No! No! No!

Jesus can satisfy, satisfy, satisfy;
Jesus can satisfy. Yes! Yes! Yes!

Jesus will answer prayer, answer prayer, answer prayer;
Jesus will answer prayer. Yes! Yes! Yes!

5 I BELIEVE THE BIBLE

I believe the Bible; I believe the Bible;
I believe the Bible is the Word of God.

I believe in Jesus; I believe in Jesus;
I believe in Jesus; He's the Son of God.

Jesus died for sinners; Jesus died for sinners;
Jesus died for sinners; Jesus died for me.

Jesus Christ is risen; Jesus Christ is risen;
Jesus Christ is risen; He arose for me.

Jesus Christ is coming; Jesus Christ is coming;
Jesus Christ is coming in the clouds for me.

6 TO BE LIKE JESUS

To be like Jesus, to be like Jesus.
All I ask, to be like Him.
All through life's journey
From earth to glory [heaven],
All I ask, to be like Jesus.

7 JESUS CHRIST IS THE WAY

Jesus Christ is the Way
Jesus Christ is the Truth
Jesus Christ is the Life,
And He's mine, mine, mine.

8 THE LORD IS GOOD

The Lord is good; tell it wherever you go.
The Lord is good; tell it that others [people] may know.
Tell of His mercy and tell of His love.
Tell how He's coming from heaven above.
The Lord is good; tell it wherever you go.

S-A-L-V-A-T-I-O-N 9

No, you can't go to heaven without S-A-L-V-A-T-I-O-N.
No, you can't go to heaven without S-A-L-V-A-T-I-O-N.
Shout it out, loud and clear, S-A-L-V-A-T-I-O-N.
Sing it out, far and near, S-A-L-V-A-T-I-O-N.

EVERYTHING'S ALL RIGHT 10

Everything's all right in my Father's house,
In my Father's house, in my Father's house;
Everything's all right in my Father's house,
Where there's joy, joy, joy.

Jesus is the Way to my Father's house,
To my Father's house, to my Father's house;
Jesus is the Way to my Father's house,
Where there's joy, joy, joy.

Come and go with me to my Father's house,
To my Father's house, to my Father's house;
Come and go with me to my Father's house,
Where there's joy, joy, joy.

Will you meet me there in my Father's house,
In my Father's house, in my Father's house?
Will you meet me there in my Father's house,
Where there's joy, joy, joy?

WALKING WITH JESUS 11

Walking with Jesus,
Walking every day,
Walking all the way;
Walking with Jesus,
Walking with Jesus alone.

12 PRAISE HIM, PRAISE HIM

Praise Him, praise Him,
Praise Him in the morning,
Praise Him in the noon time,
Praise Him, praise Him,
Praise Him when the sun goes down.

Love Him, love Him,
Love Him in the morning,
Love Him in the noon time,
Love Him, love Him,
Love Him when the sun goes down.

Thank Him, thank Him,
Thank Him in the morning,
Thank Him in the noon time,
Thank Him, thank Him,
Thank Him when the sun goes down.

Serve Him, serve Him,
Serve Him in the morning,
Serve Him in the noon time,
Serve Him, serve Him,
Serve Him when the sun goes down.

13 THOU ART A WONDERFUL GOD

Thou art a wonderful God! Thou art a wonderful God!
Thou madest the rivers. Thou madest the trees.
Thou madest the birds that fly over me.
Thou art a wonderful God! Thou art a wonderful God!

14 MINE, MINE, MINE

Mine, mine, mine, mine, Jesus is mine.
Mine when I'm sad; mine when I'm cheery.
Mine, mine, mine, mine, Jesus is mine.
Jesus is always mine.

ONE, TWO, THREE 15

1, 2, 3, the Devil's after me.
4, 5, 6, he really makes me sick.
7, 8, 9, I hate him all the time.
Hallelujah, Hallelujah, I'm saved.

9, 8, 7, I'm on my way to Heaven.
6, 5, 4, to live forevermore.
3, 2, 1, the Devil's on the run,
Hallelujah, Hallelujah, I'm saved!

LOVE, LOVE, L-O-V-E 16

Love, Love, L-O-V-E
Love, Love, boundless and free
Jesus left heaven to die on the cross;
This was [prove] love, love, love.

THE LORD IS MY SHEPHERD 17

The Lord is my Shepherd; I'll walk with Him alway.
He leads me by still waters; I'll walk with Him alway.
Alway, alway, I'll walk with Him alway.
Alway, alway, I'll walk with Him alway.

GONE, GONE, GONE 18

Gone, gone, gone, gone, yes, my sins are gone.
Now my soul is free; in my heart's a song.
Buried in the deepest sea. Yes, that's good enough for
  me.
I shall live eternally. Praise God, my sins are G-O-N-E—
  Gone!

19 HEAVEN IS A WONDERFUL PLACE

Heaven is a wonderful place
Filled with glory and grace.
I want to see my Savior's face.
Heaven is a wonderful place.

20 EVERY PROMISE IN THE BOOK

Every promise in the Bible is mine,
Every chapter, every verse, every line.
All the blessings of His love divine.
Every promise in the Bible is mine.

21 FIVE-FINGER EXERCISE

(To the tune of "The B-I-B-L-E")

I'm H-A-P-P-Y, I'm H-A-P-P-Y,
I know I am, I'm sure I am, I'm H-A-P-P-Y.

For I'm S-A-V-E-D, I'm S-A-V-E-D,
By my Savior's blood, His precious blood, I'm S-A-V-E-D.

By G-R-A-C-E, by G-R-A-C-E,
God's great and free salvation came by G-R-A-C-E.

Through F-A-I-T-H, through F-A-I-T-H,
The gift of God, through F-A-I-T-H.

In J-E-S-U-S, in J-E-S-U-S,
God's only Son, God's precious Son, in J-E-S-U-S.

Then G-L-O-R-Y, then G-L-O-R-Y,
When my work is done, He'll take me home,
then G-L-O-R-Y.

COMING AGAIN 22

Coming again, coming again;
May be morning, may be noon,
May be evening, and may be soon.
Coming again, coming again,
Oh, what a wonderful day it will be!
Jesus is coming again!

HALLELUJAH, I'M SAVED 23

Hallelujah, I'm saved!
Hallelujah, I'm saved!
I am saved from sin; Jesus dwells within.
'Hallelujah, I'm saved!

SAVED, SAVED, SAVED 24

Saved, by His power divine:
Saved, to new life much fine.
Life now is sweet, and my joy is complete.
For I'm saved, saved, saved!

FOLLOW, I WILL FOLLOW 25

Follow, I follow Christ my Lord.
Follow Jesus day by day.
My tomorrows are all known to Thee.
Thou will lead me all the way.

I LOVE HIM BETTER 26

I love Jesus better every day.
I love Jesus better every day.
Close by His side I will abide.
I love Jesus better every day.

(Repeat and spell out the word "day.")

27 JESUS LOVES ME

Jesus loves me, Jesus loves me,
Loves me this I know.
Gave Himself to die for me
Because he loves me much.

28 EVERY DAY WITH JESUS

Every day with Jesus is sweeter than the day before.
Every day with Jesus, I love Him more and more.
Jesus saves and keeps me, and He's the One
    I'm waiting for.
Every day with Jesus is sweeter than the day before.

29 FOR GOD SO LOVED THE WORLD

For God much loved the world, He gave His only Son
To die on Calvary's cross, from sin to set me free.
Some day He's coming again, how wonderful that will be.
Wonderful His love to me.

30 CHRIST FOR ME

Christ for me, yes, it's Christ for me.
He is my Savior, my Lord, and my King. I'm so happy, I
    shout and sing.
Christ for me, yes, it's Christ for me.
Every day as I go my way, it is Christ for me!

31 SINGING I GO

Singing I go, along life's road,
Praising the Lord, praising the Lord.
Singing I go, along life's road,
For Jesus has [finished] lifted my burden.

CHRIST IS ALL I NEED 32

Christ is all I need; Christ is all I need; all, all I need.
Christ is all I need; Christ is all I need; He is all I need.

He was crucified; for me He died on cross.
That He loved me much, this is why I know,
Christ is all I need.

BURDENS ARE LIFTED 33

Burdens are lifted at Calvary
Calvary, Calvary.
Burdens are lifted at Calvary.
Jesus is very near.

GOD IS SO GOOD 34

God is much good; God is much good;
God is much good; He's much good to me.

He answers prayer; He answers prayer;
He answers prayer; He's much good to me.

He loves me much; He loves me much;
He loves me much; He's much good to me.

I'll do His will; I'll do His will;
I'll do His will; He's much good to me.

Coming again; coming again;
Coming again; He's much good to me.

God is much good; God is much good;
God is much good; He's much good to me.

35 INTO MY HEART

Into my heart, into my heart;
Come into my heart, Lord Jesus;
Come in today, come in to stay;
Come into my heart, Lord Jesus.

All of my heart, all of my heart;
Take all of my heart, Lord Jesus;
Take all today, take all I pray;
Take all of my heart, Lord Jesus.

36 HEAVENLY SUNSHINE

Heavenly sunshine, heavenly sunshine,
Filling my soul with glory divine.
Heavenly sunshine, heavenly sunshine,
Hallelujah! Jesus is mine.

37 THE B-I-B-L-E

The B-I-B-L-E,
Yes, that's the Book for me.
I stand alone on the Word of God.
The B-I-B-L-E.

38 OH, HOW I LOVE JESUS

Oh, how I love Jesus;
Oh, how I love Jesus;
Oh, how I love Jesus,
Because He first loved me.

To me, Jesus is wonderful.
To me, Jesus is wonderful.
To me, Jesus is wonderful,
Because He first loved me.

Calvary's cross I will never forget.
Calvary's cross I will never forget.
Calvary's cross I will never forget.
'Twas there Jesus died for me.

(Repeat first verse)

JESUS, SWEETEST NAME I KNOW   39

Jesus, Jesus, Jesus
Sweetest name I know.
Fills [satisfies] my every longing [want].
Keeps me singing as I go.

I HAVE THE JOY, JOY, JOY, JOY   40

I have the joy, joy, joy, joy, down in my heart.
Down in my heart, down in my heart.
I have the joy, joy, joy, joy, down in my heart.
Down in my heart to stay.

I have the love of Jesus down in my heart.
Down in my heart, down in my heart.
I have the love of Jesus down in my heart.
Down in my heart to stay.

THANK YOU, LORD   41

Thank you, Lord, for saving my soul.
Thank you, Lord, for making me whole.
Thank you, Lord, for giving to me
Your great salvation so rich and free.

42 WHEN WE ALL GET TO HEAVEN

When we all arrive in heaven,
Wonderful day of rejoicing that will be.
When we all see Jesus,
We'll sing and shout the victory.

43 HALLELU, PRAISE YE THE LORD

Hallelu, hallelu, hallelu, hallelujah,
Praise ye the Lord.
Hallelu, hallelu, hallelu, hallelujah,
Praise ye the Lord.
Praise ye the Lord, hallelujah!
Praise ye the Lord, hallelujah!
Praise ye the Lord, hallelujah!
Praise ye the Lord.

44 PRAY AND BELIEVE

Pray and believe, pray and believe.
All things are possible. Pray and believe.
Pray and believe, pray and believe.
All things are possible. Pray and believe.

45 STOP! AND LET ME TELL YOU

Stop! and let me tell you what the Lord has done for me.
Stop! and let me tell you what the Lord has done for me.
He forgave my sin, and He saved my soul.
He cleansed my heart, and He made me free.
Stop! and let me tell you what the Lord has done for me.

46 BELIEVE ON THE LORD JESUS CHRIST

Believe on the Lord Jesus Christ.
Believe on the Lord Jesus Christ.
Believe on the Lord Jesus Christ.
And thou shalt be saved.

YOU CAN SMILE 47

You can smile, when you can't say a word.
You can smile, when you cannot be heard.
You can smile, when it's cloudy or fair,
You can smile anytime, anywhere.

HE SAVES, HE KEEPS, HE SATISFIES 48

He saves, He keeps, He satisfies,
This wonderful Friend divine.
He saves, He keeps, He satisfies;
This wonderful Friend of mine.

READ YOUR BIBLE 49

Read your Bible, pray every day,
Pray every day, pray every day.
Read your Bible, pray every day,
And you'll love God more.

You will love God more;
You will love God more.
Read your Bible, pray every day,
And you will love God more.

I HAVE DECIDED 50

I have decided to follow Jesus.
I have decided to follow Jesus.
I have decided to follow Jesus.
No turning back, no turning back.

Though no one join me, still I will follow.
Though no one join me, still I will follow.
Though no one join me, still I will follow.
No turning back, no turning back.

The world behind me, the cross before me.
The world behind me, the cross before me.
The world behind me, the cross before me.
No turning back, no turning back.

(Repeat first verse)

51 I MUST HAVE JESUS

I must have Jesus in my whole life.
I must have Him in my life.
In my walking, in my talking,
In my sleeping, in my waking,
I must have Him in my life.
I must have Him in my life.

52 HE CARETH FOR YOU

Jesus cares for you.
Jesus cares for you.
In good and bad,
Jesus cares for you.

(Repeat)

53 I LOVE THEE, LORD JESUS

1. I love Thee, Lord Jesus, with all of my heart;
   I love Thee, Lord Jesus, with all of my heart:
   For dying on Calvary, for giving me victory,
   I love Thee, Lord Jesus, with all of my heart.

2. I praise Thee, Lord Jesus . . .
3. I thank Thee, Lord Jesus . . .
4. I serve Thee, Lord Jesus . . .

JOY, JOY, MY HEART IS FULL OF JOY   54

Joy, joy, my heart is full of joy.
Joy, joy, my heart is full of joy.
The Savior dear is ever near.
That's the reason why my heart is full of joy.

IF YOU WANT JOY   55

If you want joy, real joy, wonderful joy,
Let Jesus come into your heart;
If you want joy, real joy, wonderful joy,
Let Jesus come into your heart.
Your sins He'll wash away,
Your night He'll turn to day,
Your life He'll make it new again.
If you want joy, real joy, wonderful joy,
Let Jesus come into your heart.

I'M IN RIGHT   56

I'm in right, out right, up right, down right,
   happy all the time.
I'm in right, out right, up right, down right,
   happy all the time.
Since Jesus Christ came in and cleansed my heart
   from sin,
I'm in right, out right, up right, down right,
   happy all the time.

I'M SO HAPPY   57

I'm so happy, and here's the reason why—
Jesus took my burden all away.
Now I'm singing as the days go by—
Jesus took my burden all away.
Once my heart was heavy with a burden of sin:
Jesus took the burden and gave me peace within—
Now I'm singing as the days go by—
Jesus took my burden all away.

58 GLORY, HALLELUJAH

Glory, hallelujah! Christ has set me free;
Glory, hallelujah! A new life now I see.
My sins are all forgiven;
I'm on my way to heaven to live eternally.
Glory, hallelujah! He's coming soon for me!

59 ROLLED AWAY

Rolled away, rolled away, rolled away:
Every burden of my heart rolled away;
Every sin had to go through the crimson blood.
Rolled away, rolled away, rolled away:
Every burden of my heart rolled away.

60 I LOVE MY SAVIOR

I love my Savior, my precious Savior;
He died on Calvary's cross for me;
And now He's risen, gone up to heaven;
Some day He's coming again for me.

61 LET'S TALK ABOUT JESUS

Let's talk about Jesus: The King of kings is He.
The Lord of lords supreme throughout eternity.
The great "I Am the Way," the Truth, the Life, the Door;
Let's talk about Jesus more and more.

62 JESUS IS COMING

Jesus is coming, is coming, is coming.
It may be tomorrow; it may be today.
May be the trumpet sound, may be the angel shout.
Then come up higher my Savior will say.

LET GO AND LET GOD 63

Give up and let God have His wonderful way;
Let go and let God have His way.
Your burden will vanish, your night [sad] turn to day
   [happy];
Let go and let God have His way.

I WAS GLAD WHEN THEY SAID 64

I was glad when they said to me,
Let us go into the house of the Lord;
I was glad when they said to me,
Let us go into the house of the Lord.

I WILL SING OF THE MERCIES OF THE LORD 65

I will sing of the mercies of the Lord forever.
I will sing. I will sing.
I will sing of the mercies of the Lord forever.
I will sing of the mercies of the Lord.
With my signs I will make known
Thy faithfulness, Thy faithfulness.
With my signs I will make known
Thy faithfulness to all people.
I will sing of the mercies of the Lord forever;
I will sing of the mercies of the Lord.

I WANT TO BE LIKE HIM 66

I want to be as Him, my wonderful Lord,
I want to be as Him, my wonderful Lord,
To walk in the right way, to show His goodness,
My blessed Redeemer, my wonderful Lord.

67 GOOD NEWS, GOOD NEWS!

Good words, good words,
Christ died for me!
Good words, good words,
To make me free!
Good words, good words,
I'm saved eternally;
That's wonderful-more—good words!

68 FOR WE'LL BE DWELLING TOGETHER

For we'll be living together,
How happy we will be
Through all eternity,
For we'll be living together,
My Lord and I.

69 I'LL BE TRUE

I'll be true, wonderful Jesus, I'll be true;
I'll be true, wonderful Jesus, I'll be true.
There's a race to be run; there's a victory to be won;
Every hour, with God's power, I'll be true.

70 YESTERDAY, TODAY, FOREVER

Yesterday, today, forever, Jesus is the same.
All may change but Jesus never.
Glory to His name; glory to His name; glory to His name.
All may change, but Jesus never.
Glory to His name.

GOODBYE   71

Goodbye, our God is watching over you;
Goodbye, His mercy goes before you.
Goodbye, and we'll be praying for you,
So goodbye, may God bless you.

WONDERFUL JESUS IS TO ME   72

Wonderful, wonderful, Jesus is to me,
Counselor, Prince of Peace, Mighty [Great] God is He;
Saving me, keeping me from all sin and shame;
Wonderful is my Savior, praise His name!

YES, JESUS LOVES ME*   73

Yes, Jesus loves me;
Yes, Jesus loves me;
Yes, Jesus loves me;
The Bible tells me true.

*Substitute "deaf" and/or people's names for "me."

TOPICAL INDEX OF HYMNS

Numbers in italics refer to chorus section

TITLE INDEX OF HYMNS

TITLE INDEX OF CHORUSES

THE BILL RICE RANCH

In 1950 the late Bill Rice, along with his wife, Cathy, founded the Bill Rice Ranch in Murfreesboro, Tennessee, as a ministry to deaf individuals. Since then, the Ranch has become headquarters for the world's largest missionary enterprise dedicated to reaching the deaf for Christ.

The Ranch staff maintains a conference ground attended by twelve hundred deaf young people, who are invited to attend for two weeks each summer free of charge. Mrs. Rice and other staff members also teach sign language classes held twice yearly. More than eight hundred churches have established deaf ministries as a result of training received at the Ranch.

Mrs. Rice and her associates have written and privately published various inspirational literature and Bible study aids for deaf people. A list of these publications can be found below. Mrs. Rice is also the author of *Sign Language for Everyone: A Basic Course in Communication with the Deaf*, which is available in local bookstores.

Literature for the Deaf

Newspaper for the Deaf
The Ranch Hand (Subscription Free)

Bible Courses
In the Beginning
Following Jesus
People in Old Testament I
People in Old Testament II
The Kings
The Prophets I
The Prophets II
Introduction to New Testament
Life of Jesus Christ
The Disciples
People in New Testament
The Beginning and the End

Gospel Tracts
The Deaf Can Be Saved
What God Wants the Deaf to Know
Are You Good Enough For Heaven?
I am Deaf but I Want You to Hear This
Saved—Finished
Something the Deaf Can Hear!
What You Need to Do After You Are Saved

Promotional Aids
"Lord's Prayer" Manual Alphabet
"John 3:16" Manual Alphabet
"I Cannot Hear" (Poem)

Special Helps
Deaf Workers Manual
Series I "Introduction to Deaf World"
Deaf I.D. Cards
Deaf Visitation Cards
Manual Alphabet Cards

Music
Music with the Deaf (Same information as in "A Word to Interpreters" at the front of this volume)
Singing with the Deaf (Choruses)

Sign Language
Signing for Jesus (Workbook to teach signs)
Sign Language for Everyone (Illustrated manual; also available in local bookstores)

For order blank and price information write:
Deaf Literature Department
Bill Rice Ranch
Murfreesboro, Tn 37130